Late
at Night

Written by Paul Hamlyn
Illustrated by Annabel Spenceley

I saw a roof.

I saw a cat.

I saw a star.

I saw a bat.

I saw a car.

I saw a tree.

I saw two eyes

and they saw me.

I saw a roof.
I saw a cat.
I saw a star.
I saw a bat.
I saw a car.
I saw a tree.
I saw two eyes
and they saw me.

Your
Horoscope
2020

. . . .

Sagittarius

Your
Horoscope
2020

....

Sagittarius

23rd November - 21st December

igloobooks

igloobooks

Published in 2019
by Igloo Books Ltd
Cottage Farm
Sywell
NN6 0BJ
www.igloobooks.com

Copyright © 2018 Igloo Books Ltd
Igloo Books is an imprint of Bonnier Books UK

0819 001.01
2 4 6 8 10 9 7 5 3 1
ISBN 978-1-78905-717-1

Written by Belinda Campbell and Denise Evans

Cover design by Dave Chapman
Edited by Bobby Newlyn-Jones

Printed and manufactured in China

CONTENTS

· · · · · · · · · · · · · · · · ·

INTRODUCTION
··················

This horoscope has been specifically created to allow
you to get the most from astrological patterns and
the way they have a bearing on not only your zodiac
sign, but nuances within it. Using the diary section
of the book you can read about the influences and
possibilities of each and every day of the year. It will
be possible for you to see when you are likely to be
cheerful and happy or those times when your nature
is in retreat and you will be more circumspect. The
diary will help to give you a feel for the specific
'cycles' of astrology and the way they can subtly
change your day-to-day life.

THE CHARACTER OF THE ARCHER

. . . .

A sign that loves to wonder and wander, Sagittarians
are the explorers of the zodiac, both in their minds
and around the globe. Born in the ninth house of the
zodiac calendar that signifies growth, progress for the
sake of progress is not what this sign stands for, as
the journey itself will be important to this meaningful
traveller, not just the destination. The Sagittarian's
quest for adventure, be it intellectual or physical, can
be unquenchable because their element, Fire, needs
constantly fuelling to keep its flames burning bright.
This sign can certainly shine brighter than most, ruled
by the largest and third brightest planet in the sky.
Named after the Roman ruler of gods, Jupiter makes
sure that Sagittarians live with confidence and luck
on their side; or perhaps it's not luck, but the hand
of a higher being, as this sign can be highly spiritual
or religious. Whether it's the good fortune of wealth,
happiness, family, or faith this sunny sign will find
something in their life that makes them feel lucky to
be alive.

Born at the end of autumn, Sagittarians are mutable
and are perhaps the most open-minded to change of
all the signs. Openness can breed honesty, which is
perhaps why Sagittarians are commonly known as the
zodiac's truth-tellers. Honesty is this sign's best policy,
but their blunt delivery can sometimes need finessing.
The Centaur Archer that symbolises Sagittarius can be

an indicator of this sign's daring attitude and physical strength. With a positive energy that embraces physical challenges, Sagittarians can make fearless sports figures, like Eddie the Eagle with his record-breaking ski stunts. Above all, this sign can be an icon of inspiration, from Britney Spears to Winston Churchill, and at their core Sagittarians can motivate, bring joy, and encourage positive change.

THE CENTAUR ARCHER

Mind of a man and body of a beast, the mythological symbol of the Centaur is one of the dual signs in the zodiac. As with any dual sign, like Gemini's twins and Pisces' two fishes, there are usually two sides to them. With Sagittarians it is usually divided as their Centaur symbol suggests, by the mind and body. This sign is full of influential thinkers from William Blake to daring athletic personalities like Bruce Lee (who was also a known philosopher). The Archer signifies many of a Sagittarian's qualities: strong, daring, but perhaps none more so than this optimistic sign's ability to always look to the future. Sagittarians' aim can strike true first time, with the luck of the ruling planet Jupiter, or can dramatically miss. But fail or succeed, this hopeful sign is the embodiment of not giving up. The Archer can be dangerous, so risk-taking is usually common for many Sagittarians. As with any wild animal, the Centaur can at times feel restless, especially if they feel caged in any way. Sagittarians need to roam freely both in the mind and body to achieve their fullest potential.

JUPITER

Ruled by the largest planet in the sky, Sagittarians are hard to miss. They are named after Jupiter, the ruler of the gods in Roman mythology, who ruled over the sky and was usually depicted holding his trident of lightening. For most Sagittarians, the sky's the limit and they will live their lives with optimism and the desire to broaden their horizons. The sky is an important symbol in many religions and soul-searching Sagittarians may have a strong spiritual or religious faith. Jupiter is the fastest spinning planet in the solar system, resulting in it having the shortest days of all the planets, which perhaps explains Sagittarians' restlessness and desire to live each minute to its fullest. Jupiter is well known for having a red spot, which we now know to be a continuously raging storm. Whilst Sagittarians don't often lose their temper, this red spot on their ruling planet could be an indicator that when this sign is angry, it will be visible for everyone to see. Jupiter is associated with good luck, and with a daring Fire sign like Sagittarius, fortune is likely to favour this brave sign.

ELEMENTS, MODES AND POLARITIES

Each sign is made up of a unique combination of three defining groups: elements, modes and polarities. Each of these defining parts can manifest themselves in good and bad ways and none should be seen to be a positive or a negative – including the polarities! Just like a jigsaw puzzle, piecing these groups together can help illuminate why each sign has certain characteristics and help us to find a balance.

ELEMENTS

Fire: Dynamic and adventurous, signs with Fire in them can be extroverted. Others are naturally drawn to them because of the positive light they give off, as well as their high levels of energy and confidence.

Earth: Signs with the Earth element are steady and driven with their ambitions. They make for a solid friend, parent or partner due to their grounded influence and nurturing nature.

Air: The invisible element that influences each of the other elements significantly, Air signs will provide much-needed perspective to others with their fair thinking, verbal skills and key ideas.

Water: Warm in the shallows and freezing as ice. This mysterious element is essential to the growth of everything around it, through its emotional depth and empathy.

MODES

Cardinal: Pioneers of the calendar, cardinal signs jump-start each season and are the energetic go-getters.

Fixed: Marking the middle of the calendar, fixed signs firmly denote and value steadiness and reliability.

Mutable: As the seasons end, the mutable signs adapt and give themselves over gladly to the promise of change.

POLARITIES

Positive: Typically extroverted, positive signs take physical action and embrace outside stimulus in their life.

Negative: Usually introverted, negative signs value emotional development and experiencing life from the inside out.

SAGITTARIANS IN BRIEF

The table below shows the key attributes of Sagittarians. Use it for quick reference and to understand more about this fascinating sign.

SYMBOL	RULING PLANET	MODE	ELEMENT	HOUSE
♐	♃	△	△	IX
The Centaur Archer	Jupiter	Mutable	Fire	Ninth

COLOUR	BODY PART	POLARITY	GENDER	POLAR SIGN
		⊕	♂	II
Purple	Hips, Thighs, Liver	Positive	Masculine	Gemini

LOVE
....

Like a moth to the flame, this Fire sign draws lovers into its inviting light purely by being its dynamic and sociable Sagittarian self. Confident Sagittarians are not shy of taking the lead and braving it alone, but if they can find a partner to take on their endless journeys then they can experience their greatest adventures yet. A relationship that does not compromise their individuality in any way will be essential: a Sagittarian will not happily sacrifice their own dreams for others, like, for example, Pisceans often do. They will also abhor any signs of possessiveness from their partner, so Scorpio or Taurus lovers could be problematic. Sagittarians may have trouble committing to the one partner if they feel that the relationship is binding their freedom in any way. Learning to share their time and the art of compromising will be two tricky areas in love that this sign may need to work harder at.

With free-roaming Sagittarians, the grass can have a habit of always looking greener and they may be inclined to eagerly wander from one relationship to another. If they want to find a long-lasting love that keeps the passions of their Fire element burning night after night, then finding a like-minded intellectual or outdoorsy explorer to share their life with will be key. Air signs will not only keep this Fire sign burning, they are also associated with the mind and ideas so could make ideal partners for a Sagittarian looking for mental stimulation from their partner. A stimulating spouse is a must, as is finding common interests, which for this positive sign may mean adventures in the great outdoors like holidays spent wild camping and roasting marshmallows on a campfire. A sign that has a matching positive energy will have a good chance of keeping up physically with this wild Centaur. Fundamentally, this forward-thinking Archer could benefit most from an open-minded partner with whom they can see a future.

ARIES: COMPATIBILITY 5/5

If Aries gets struck by one of Sagittarius' arrows it will be a sure sign of Cupid's work. This couple's compatibility is high due to their matching positivity and lively personalities. Aries may have finally found their true match in risk-taking Sagittarius. With a shared love of travel, there's unlikely to be any Sagittarius adventure that the Aries would pass up on. These two are go-getters and if they can find shared interests then this partnership is an ideal match of two pioneering signs, the Ram and Centaur happily galloping side by side.

TAURUS: COMPATIBILITY 2/5

Sagittarius is ruled by the planet Jupiter which is associated with luck, something that a Taurus doesn't always believe in, valuing hard work more. Whilst a Sagittarian values new experiences, Taureans can prefer the comforts of what they know. The biggest struggle that this Fire and Earth couple may have is Sagittarius' need for freedom and Taurus' tendency towards possessiveness with their partners. A claustrophobic atmosphere should be avoided, and freedom generously given in this relationship. Learn from each other, admire the faster gallop of the Centaur and equally appreciate the steady plod of the Bull.

GEMINI: COMPATIBILITY 5/5

'I love you just the way you are,' could be the vows of strongly independent signs Sagittarius and Gemini. Despite being both mutable signs that are open to adapt, there is unlikely to be anything about this match that either partner will want to change about the other. Being opposite signs on the zodiac calendar, the bond between Sagittarius and Gemini is usually going to be unique. For a sign that can become easily bored like Gemini, the adventurous Sagittarian is a perfect fit and will ensure this couple have endless days of love and fun ahead of them.

CANCER: COMPATIBILITY 1/5

The homebody Cancer might end up feeling lost with the adventuring wanderer that is Sagittarius. Daring Sagittarians can help bring out a worldlier side to Cancerians and teach them that their sense of community can stretch larger than the end of their road. With Cancer, the roaming Sagittarius can learn the benefits of settling down in a loving relationship. These two have contrasting masculine and feminine energies that can complement each other greatly if their differences are nurtured rather than discouraged. Give each other plenty of room to be and reap the many rewards from when opposites attract.

LEO: COMPATIBILITY 4/5

With two Fire signs like adventurous Sagittarius and
spontaneous Leo, theirs is a love that will surely spark
with excitement. Here is a couple that should keep
their passports to hand as either one is likely to plan
a surprise romantic getaway for the other with little or
no notice. Leo and Sagittarius match each other with
their positive energies and are probably the dynamic
couple that is at the top of every party invite list. The
philosophical Sagittarius and purpose-led Leo can share
a powerful bond whose influence could be felt well
beyond them.

VIRGO: COMPATIBILITY 2/5

Whilst the outdoorsy Sagittarius and Earth sign Virgo
both have a strong love for being outside in nature, they
have some serious core differences, such as Virgo's love
for routine and Sagittarians' dislike of the same; so these
two lovers may have their work cut out for them. The
wild Centaur can sometimes feel too reckless for the
over-thinking Virgo as they bolt heart-first after their
goals, whilst a Sagittarian might feel that the Virgoan's
overactive mind is slowing them down. Find some
common ground, and this mutable pair could experience
an honest and thought-provoking relationship.

LIBRA: COMPATIBILITY 4/5

The good fortune of Sagittarius' Jupiter and the love of
Libra's Venus could make these two lucky in love together.
Fire sign Sagittarius and Air sign Libra are sure to get each

other hot under the collar with their complimentary elements helping to keep their passions burning. Both high energy positive signs, they should have no problem keeping up with each other's packed social schedules and will share plenty of adventures. The tactful Libra and sometimes blunt Sagittarius could clash if their ideas of commitment don't match, but they have a good chance of working out their differences and happily moving forward together.

SCORPIO: COMPATIBILITY 2/5

Sagittarius and Scorpio can have a daring partnership: whether their gamble on each other pays off is another thing entirely. The adventurous Sagittarian will help expand Scorpio's horizons and appeal to their brave side, whilst Scorpio's fixed attitude can teach the flaky Sagittarian to stay motivated and see things through. The love of Scorpio can be all encompassing and the worst thing for a Sagittarian is for them to feel like their partner is at all possessive. This is definitely not a boring love, but flexibility and growth are both key for these two getting the most out of the relationship.

SAGITTARIUS: COMPATIBILITY 4/5

An honest and awe-inspiring couple, these two lively
Sagittarian intellects can have a fiery love. If any couple
stood a chance with making a long-distance relationship
work, it would be these two independent spirits. Two
Sagittarian lovers will understand the importance of
each other's independence so will be accustomed to
giving each other as much breathing space as necessary.
Their mutable natures make them flexible and ready for
big changes in the relationship, whether it's moving to
another country or starting a family. This is a pair that
can inspire, spark, and dare one another to reach the
highest of heights.

CAPRICORN: COMPATIBILITY 2/5

A materialist Capricorn and dazzling Sagittarius can
both be guilty of feeling a little superior, which won't
do in a partnership, especially when these two can
have such different approaches to life. The rational
Capricorn may be fearful of going to daring heights
with their lively Sagittarius partner but if they are open
to Sagittarius' optimism, they could learn to love more
bravely. Sagittarius may feel constrained by Capricorn's
constant reminder that actions have consequences,
but looking before they leap could be a vital lesson
for a Capricorn to teach their Sagittarian partner. The
key to their happiness will be embracing each other's
opposites.

AQUARIUS: COMPATIBILITY 4/5

Placed two apart on the zodiac calendar, the positive energies of an Aquarian and Sagittarian can be a complementary and exciting love match. The thrilling ideas of a Sagittarius combined with the Aquarian's independent thinking can mean that these stimulating spouses will have plenty to talk about. The Fire in Sagittarius brings an enthusiastic energy to the relationship and the fixed mode of Aquarius can help provide a focus to their ideas and bring them to fruition. Communal-minded Aquarius and sociable Sagittarius will likely be at the heart of their shared communities and bring great meaning to each other's lives.

PISCES: COMPATIBILITY 3/5

The roaming Sagittarius and the escapist Pisces could end up blissfully running off into the sunset together if they can learn from each other's differences. Both ruled by Jupiter, these two may indeed have been lucky to find one another. Jupiter gives Sagittarians and Pisceans a zest for life and their shared mutable modes will make their relationship open to continuous growth and change. Pisceans can lack the active side that many Fire signs have, whilst Sagittarians can lack compassion which could lead to clashes with this sensitive Water sign. Focus on common interests and this deep pair could go far.

FAMILY AND FRIENDS

. . . .

Friends and family of a Sagittarian should be ready to get taken on a journey. Whether it's road-tripping down Route 66 or escaping to a meditation retreat, a Sagittarian can inspire both physical journeys and mental ones, as their duality of the Centaur (half man, half horse) suggests. Yoga mat at the ready, Water sign and spiritual Piscean friends or family members can make the perfect partner to go in search of higher meaning and mindful enlightenment with. For more physical adventures, the active Fire sign of Aries will rise to a sporty Sagittarian's challenge and race them to the top of any mountain. It's not all about the thrill of life that urges this sign on in their constant state of exploration: Sagittarians enjoy finding meaning in the world and what they do. As the charitable Sagittarian races over the marathon finishing line in their banana costume, their philanthropic Cancerian friends and family members are sure to be there cheering and offering their generous support.

A Sagittarian is a known truth-teller and sometimes their candid words of advice can be felt deeply by their sensitive family and friends. Whilst honesty is an admirable quality, the way in which Sagittarians deliver their wise words to their loved ones may need some work. Scorpio is a daring friend that may be close to a Sagittarian, and whilst the Scorpion is made of hardy stuff, any Water sign has a sensitive soul that the blunt words of a Sagittarian should be wary of damaging if they want to hold on to their friendships. Expert communicator Gemini and diplomatic Libra may be able to help their Sagittarian friend word things in a more tactful way so that their words inspire rather than injure. The famous writer and Sagittarius Dale Carnegie, who wrote *How to Win Friends and Influence People*, shows just how influential the voice of a Sagittarian can be when delivered in a positive way.

Should the studious Sagittarius wish to start their own family, their love for learning will no doubt be something that they will want to pass on to their children. Sagittarians can make wonderful teachers, whether it's teaching their child to throw a ball or learn a new language; for the travelling Sagittarian, they may decide to bring their children up in a foreign country to truly broaden their horizons and give them their first taste of adventure. The Archer looks to the future, and as a parent the future of their children could be of utmost important to this sign; planning which schools they will attend, enrolling them in sports clubs, teaching them piano may all be things that the forward-thinking Sagittarian partner thinks about early on as they encourage their child to explore their full potential. As their children grow up, and even when they become adults, the Sagittarius parent will continue to try and challenge their children and impart their wisdom.

MONEY AND CAREERS

. . . .

Being a certain star sign will not dictate the type of career that you have, although the characteristics that fall under each sign could help you identify the areas in which you could potentially thrive. Conversely, to succeed in the workplace, it is just as important to understand what you are good at as it is to know what you are less brilliant at so that you can see the areas in which you will need to perhaps work harder to achieve your career and financial goals.

Sagittarians understand the preciousness of time, remember Jupiter has the shortest days of all the planets, so they might not work well with colleagues prone to dithering. As a boss, Sagittarians can be inspiring, but they can also be preachy, impatient and downright mean in their critique. Sagittarians should try to appreciate that not everyone works at the same fast pace as them (Virgos especially like taking their time over projects) and what feels obvious to them sometimes needs to be pointed out to others. Sagittarians can continue to inspire by showing compassion and patience and always offering to help those that need help.

Clear career paths such as studying law, going to filmmaking school, or practising to become a singer could suit the Archer who has a clear aim in life. Caged within the confines of an office might not suit all Sagittarians, so finding a career that has travel prospects could appeal to this wild traveller. This highly sociable sign may enjoy a career that allows them to speak to the masses, whether it's as an academic lecturer that uses their intellect or a spiritual or religious leader that brings meaning to life. The most influential Sagittarians in their professional field, such as Steven Spielberg, Jimi Hendrix, or Taylor Swift, are well loved because they have followed their dreams and help to inspire others to do the same.

The thrill-seeking Sagittarian may need to keep their wild spending in check and always use their heads when looking to invest or gamble their money, especially if they don't have endless funds to play with. Sagittarians may be interested in more high-risk investments but, being born in the ninth house of progression, they are also a fan of seeing things grow so a more secure financial venture could bring equal satisfaction as they are more likely to see their money grow steadily but surely. If lucky Jupiter is shining down on them, Sagittarians may find themselves galloping to the races with an uncanny ability to pick out the strongest horses thanks to their inner Centaur.

Whilst you can't always choose who you work with,
it can be advantageous to learn about colleagues' key
characteristics through their star signs to try and work
out the best ways of working with them. Leos can be led
by a purpose, similar to Sagittarians' quest to find truth,
so may be an influential colleague to help this sign find
meaning in their work. If this wanderer is feeling a little
lost, Earth signs like Capricorn and Virgo could help
them feel more grounded. The fixed Earth sign of Taurus
could clash initially with a Sagittarius, however their
strong work ethic and steadfast approach to their goals
could help this mutable sign achieve theirs also.

HEALTH AND WELLBEING
··················

Whilst Sagittarians don't often lose their temper, the red tempestuous spot that storms constantly on their ruling planet of Jupiter can be an indicator of the public outbursts that this sign can be capable of. Sagittarian Britney Spears was known only for her singing and sunny southern charm until she was hounded by the paparazzi to the brink of a breakdown. Bald Britney in 2007 is an extreme example of when a Sagittarian dramatically loses their nerve in public. The positivity of Sagittarians is a noble quality, however, this dual sign has ups and downs just like the rest of the world and cannot be expected to be all smiles. Learning how to release any upset in a positive way, whether it be through attending therapy, writing poetry, or trying out a boxercise class, is important for any sign and something that Sagittarians should not neglect.

For anyone that is prone to taking risks, they understand that danger is an inevitable part of the thrill. For Sagittarians, their physical activities may include hazardous sports like mountaineering or even being a stunt double. If risk is part of a Sagittarian's daily job or an aspect of their hobby, this sign may need to take extra care of their physical and mental health so that their body and mind can endure the extra stresses put upon it. Practising yoga and meditation could be helpful exercises for bringing strength and calmness to their action-packed life. If a Sagittarian is too restless for yoga, channelling the Archer in them could be a perfect way of satisfying their need for danger in the safety of a controlled environment of an archery class.

Sagittarians are usually sociable creatures and the life and soul of any party, which might have them out drinking and partying regularly. Over-indulging can be a problem for some born under this sign and with the liver being the part of the body that Sagittarians are associated with, hangovers could be particularly unpleasant for them, or at least that might be their excuse for staying in bed. Keeping a broad variety of friends will help a Sagittarian's social calendar have a healthier balance of partying and relaxation time. The invite for tea at a Taurean's house is just as important as the Leo friend that always has tickets for premiers or nightclub openings.

For Sagittarians that feel the Centaur running strongly inside of them, spending time outdoors will be of huge importance to their physical and mental health. For a sign that is constantly on the move like wildfire, taking a slow walk to soak up the wonders of Mother Nature could help soothe their racing mind. For city Sagittarians, reading their book in a park or signing up for an outdoor bootcamp class could help bring them back to earth. Some Sagittarians may find that they have an affinity with horses and that the feeling of countryside air rushing past their cheeks gives them the greatest pleasure. If this sign is so inclined, horse riding will have the double benefit of bringing them joy and a level of fitness.

Sagittarius

....

2020
DIARY PAGES

JANUARY

Wednesday 1st
Happy New Year, Sagittarius! This year begins with a family theme. Celebrations with your loved ones fill your heart with a sense of belonging. There is a need for you to find your place and discover what family means to you. You are the dreamer of your tribe.

Thursday 2nd
Money talks, Sagittarius. The chatty planet Mercury is boasting and inflating his ego in your money sector. Mercury is connecting to Jupiter who makes things bigger. Overspending is possible in the high street sales. Be careful not to boast about what you own and earn. No-one likes a show-off.

Friday 3rd
There is an urgency now to get to the bottom of something deep. Passive-aggressive behaviour can be apparent. Be direct and honest but avoid hostility. Mars in the last degree of your dreams sector is responsible for this. Do not push your dreams and visions onto others.

Saturday 4th

Mars now moves into your sign. This is the area of 'self'
and how you present yourself. Negotiation is not on the
agenda. You know what you want and go after it. This
is a no-compromise zone but try to get what you want
without aggression. Tact and diplomacy go further.

Sunday 5th

The Moon enters your health and daily duties sector.
Here you can be stubborn or dedicated. Thinking about
your routines getting back to normal can be depressing
after the holiday season. This is also the time to check
in with your health as you may have over-indulged on
holiday food.

Monday 6th

Planets in Earth's energy pull you back down to the
daily grind. The new year brings new thoughts about
money and possessions. You need to fight the urge
to re-furnish your entire home. Right now, you feel
determined to be careful with your finances. But how
long will this last?

Tuesday 7th

Two planets in your money sector are sitting together today. Saturn has lessons for you and Pluto needs you to take back control. Restrictions and blockages with finances will feature all week. You must learn where the boundaries are. Something needs to change, and this will be a theme all year.

Wednesday 8th

There is a little devil on your shoulder telling you to spend money on some short trips today. Do not pay any attention. This is Venus, who likes luxury and rules money. Hers is not the voice you need to hear right now. Ignore her and keep your money in your wallet.

Thursday 9th

Today your important relationships are on your mind. Partners or lovers want to reconnect. This can be a lovely day for romantic connections or simply a time to acknowledge all sides of yourself. The Moon in this sector can also bring out your darker, more shadowy side.

Friday 10th

The first Full Moon of the year falls in your sector of sex, death and rebirth. A lunar eclipse throws a shadow over something in this area. Mothers, maternal ancestors and nurturing also feature now. What have you achieved with these issues in the last six months? This sector holds deep secrets.

Saturday 11th

Uranus, known as the disruptor planet, goes direct today and gives you a breather in your duties sector. Health problems may ease or be resolved altogether now that all planets are direct. Any unrest in your daily routine can be smoothed over. You want an easy time in your daily routines.

Sunday 12th

Everybody seems to have an opinion on how you should use your money. You will be overwhelmed today with conversations, arguments and control issues. Anger could bubble up in you and will make you run away or let out a big roar and let people know who is the boss.

Monday 13th

These issues around money just keep coming. The Sun now meets up with the planets influencing your finances and throws light on the problems. You may have an 'aha' moment where you can see solutions. Use the Sun's energy to express concerns and make your voice heard.

Tuesday 14th

Venus glides into your family sector. Here she will add love, beauty and harmony but make no mistake, she also loves money and luxury. Family matters that involve more spending are not right for you now. Use her energy to maintain balance and share the family love for each other.

Wednesday 15th

The Moon is in your career sector. This is great news
as there is now the chance to be methodical and
meticulous. Paying attention to all the details in your
career is one of your strengths. This strength can now be
transferred to issues in your money sector.

Thursday 16th

Today you feel like being out with friends or connecting
on social media groups. However, the communication
planet, Mercury, is asking you to make last-minute
checks in your money sector. Do not be persuaded
to make an impulse buy today as you will regret it.
Families can be temperamental now.

Friday 17th

Expect conversations to be a little quirky for the
next couple of weeks. Mercury has entered your
communications sector and will be thinking, talking and
speaking on the most bizarre of topics. You could find
yourself being quite the revolutionary now. People will
listen to what you have to say.

Saturday 18th

The Moon enters your dreams sector and you could be moody and intense today. Words can come out of your mouth before you even think about them. Spontaneous revelations or gossip may come your way. Does this sound like you? Think twice before saying something that may not be received well.

Sunday 19th

The depths of your subconscious can be accessed today by the Moon's connection to Pluto and Saturn. You will feel like pushing your own boundaries and stepping outside your comfort zone. This is great news, because this is how you grow. You are not afraid of the unknown.

Monday 20th

You will feel more like yourself today. The Moon enters your sign and you want to get out and stay out. The brief stay in your inner world was quite enough. Energy levels get a boost by the Moon meeting Mars and you are ready to aim your arrows.

Tuesday 21st

The Sun is now in your communications sector.
This adds to the energy of Mercury and gives you
the gift of the gab. You could sell ice to Iceland if you
wanted to. This is the time when your ideas become
innovative. You may be making a lot of short trips now.

Wednesday 22nd

Beware of an overly emotional response to problems.
When the Moon enters your money sector, it is also
connecting with food and luxury. You may over-indulge at
these times as a way of avoiding your responsibilities or
any issues regarding the home, your self-worth or finances.

Thursday 23rd

If you are moody and emotional now, do not binge on
purchases to make you feel better. This year, Jupiter
stays in your money sector and each month when the
Moon passes you will feel this urge. There is a danger of
building up debt this year. Practise grounding exercises
or yoga at these times.

Friday 24th

Today there is a New Moon in your communications
sector. You can make mini-resolutions about issues in
this area or plant seeds of intention. There will be power
struggles today between men and women. Mars in your
own sign can make you feel aggressive.

Saturday 25th

This is another day where you can get what you want.
Mercury and Mars are making a great connection with
each other, which makes it possible for you to sweet-talk
anyone into doing your bidding. Make the most of
this opportunity.

Sunday 26th

The Moon comes to visit Mercury who is wheeling
and dealing in your communications sector. You are
emotionally attached to what you say today. You speak
with passion and can mesmerise anyone who is listening.
If you have a soapbox, get it out and make a speech.

Monday 27th

Be careful today. The Moon is in a dreamy sign which
can make things seem nicer than they are. Venus is also
connecting to Neptune who rules dreams and illusions.
All this energy combined can be beautiful but can also
be a mirage. Do not get fooled today.

Tuesday 28th

Where do you sacrifice yourself for others? This is likely
to happen in your family of origin where you may have
been the scapegoat or otherwise taken for granted. You
can be made use of because you lack the necessary
boundaries for a healthy relationship. Today is the day to
make note of this.

Wednesday 29th

You step out of the fog and into a more positive frame
of mind. Self-expression and creativity receive a boost
and you are seen and heard now. You might want to start
something new today. Love interests also appear on your
radar, although this may be projects, not people.

Thursday 30th

Today you are in a holding space where you look back
to the past and forward to the future. You consider a
past love and wonder if it is worth resurrecting. Think
carefully, as you may just be dragging up dead weight
when there is something new waiting for you.

Friday 31st

As the Moon shifts, it connects to Saturn and Pluto
who give you the answer you were seeking yesterday.
You must learn to respect the personal boundaries of
someone. There will be power struggles if you do not.
This will backfire on you unless you tread carefully.

FEBRUARY

·················

Saturday 1st

Has your daily routine become at all boring? Today you want to shake things up and do it a bit differently. Even if you do not want to do this, you may find that it will be done for you. There can be a shock or surprise today and this will upset the status quo.

Sunday 2nd

Your finances get a boost today. You may also be getting a tighter rein on your spending. There is an easy energy flow between your daily routines and money. Women will get their own way today and you could be easily persuaded to make a change of some sort.

Monday 3rd

Mercury is in the last critical degree of your communications and short trips sector. Is there anything you have overlooked concerning these areas? Sort this out now before Mercury moves on. Your emotions are with your partner or inner lover today. A little romance will be good for you now.

Tuesday 4th

Families and mothers now get the Mercury influence.
There will be a lot of talking, listening and laughter in
your family group. Stories are shared and grievances
aired. If there is anything you need to get off your chest,
do it while Mercury is here.

Wednesday 5th

Your emotions and actions are not in sync today and
you cannot be bothered to do much. There is a conflict
between maternal and paternal figures, which can
include bosses at work. There may be some family
secrets coming out that surprise you. Try not to be the
one who spills the beans.

Thursday 6th

The Moon joins a point in the sky associated with
destiny. For you Sagittarius, this concerns sex, death and
rebirth. You may be thinking about bringing something
to closure or starting something new. This must be
something which brings you comfort. If it does not, then
let it go.

Friday 7th

You will be drawn to thinking about your finances and
your home environment. What is no longer giving you
pleasure in these areas? Is there something that you can
transform into a thing of beauty? Venus is urging you to
spend time with a neglected family member.

Saturday 8th

There is a lot of Fire energy around today. You are comfortable with this and it suits your agenda. The Moon hits your travel sector whilst Venus moves into your creative sector. Put on your explorer's hat and go on an adventure, even if it is just in your mind.

Sunday 9th

A Full Moon in your travel sector highlights the need for you to express your unique self through exploration and discovery. Higher education is where you have a chance to shine, as it brings you closer to foreign lands and cultures. Have you managed to do anything about this in the last six months?

Monday 10th

Back to work after the weekend and your emotions are stabilised by your routines and career obligations. Setting your mind to a task and working steadily on it brings you the greatest satisfaction. You like to be of service at work and people can rely on you to get the job done.

Tuesday 11th

Easy connections from the Moon to all the planets in your money sector means that you are in a place where your bank balance is doing ok. This will not always be the case so look at how you have achieved this today and take note for future struggles.

Wednesday 12th

Social connections of all sorts can make you happy today. Groups of friends in real life or on social media are active and lively now. You reminisce on friends past and present and may experience some moments of regret or resentment. This is just a passing moon phase.

Thursday 13th

Today you are a bit reckless and upset that nice bank balance. Going out with friends can be great fun for you, but do you really have to spend that much? This is a tough year for finances - you must be frugal now and spend in later months.

Friday 14th

The Moon enters the most secret part of your chart. This time of the month is where you can isolate yourself on purpose and be alone with your thoughts. It's not a bad thing to want to switch off for a while and find a bit of inner calm.

Saturday 15th

The first Mercury retrograde of the year is almost here. Back up all your devices now and avoid signing contracts. Double-check any travel plans. This can be a disruptive time and tempers may flare through frustration. Time to re-do or review the last three weeks.

Sunday 16th

Mars has left your sign and you may feel an energy
drop. He will now be joining the planets in your
money house so expect some aggressive money-making
ideas to surface. You may also be changing your home
environment around now. You will also be on the move a
lot but be mindful of the Mercury retrograde.

Monday 17th

So, Mercury retrograde begins. This will occur in
your family sector Sagittarius. Take extra care not to
upset your nearest and dearest. There may be some
unnecessary sacrifices made which you will regret later.
Strengthen your boundaries now and keep them healthy.
Be kind and tactful.

Tuesday 18th

Jupiter, the planet that makes things bigger, is
connecting to Neptune, the planet that rules dreams and
illusions. The two of these together can make illusions
huge. You may be dazzled into believing an untruth
today Sagittarius. Stay grounded and Earthed. You need
to be on this planet today Sagittarius.

Wednesday 19th

The Sun enters your family sector for a month. This
will help to burn away any fog or illusions caused by
Neptune. Family truths will be revealed this month.
Father figures will feature strongly now and there could
be some manipulation. Overall, the Sun adds warmth
and joyfulness.

Thursday 20th

Today your emotions may be unstable. Doubt about
your ability to stay above water with your finances
weighs on you. There are three heavy duty planets
in this sector bringing luck (or karma), lessons and
change. You must learn what they are teaching, or you
are at risk of sinking.

Friday 21st

Mars is charging through your money and possessions
sector and has decided to de-clutter. Be prepared to lose
what is not serving you. Items bought on a whim may
now be sold. Mars wants success, so he is doing his best
to help while here.

Saturday 22nd

The Moon has escaped the heaviness of your money
sector and moves into your communications sector.
Here she wants to spread the love, get emotional and
hug everyone. Make short trips to visit people now as
this will comfort you. There will be some nice surprises
within the family now.

Sunday 23rd

There is a New Moon today in your family sector. It is in a sign that rules dreams, endings and merging with God. This is a great time to set new intentions and affirmations regarding family, mothers, and ancestors. You can bring something to loving closure now.

Monday 24th

Venus is the Warrior Goddess in your creativity sector. Here she can start a project and see it through to the end. She can also stand up and be a leader. Today, she is squaring off with Jupiter in your money house. She is unhappy with his overspending.

Tuesday 25th

Whilst Mars is driving his chariot through your money sector, he stops to look back at how far he has come. He is asking you to remember skills that you have which may be useful now regarding money and your home environment. Are you any good at buying and selling?

Wednesday 26th

Did you forget about the Mercury retrograde? Today he is in the glare of the Sun and is speechless for once. Here he receives new information and needs more processing time. What new information have you learned about your family of origin? What new thought patterns do you have?

Thursday 27th

You have more motivation today and can see a way forward. Your mind is full of plans that bring a sense of positivity and optimism. Think all this through and re-check every detail before putting this into action. Wait until after Mercury goes direct again.

Friday 28th

Today you must check in with your health and fitness. There has been a lot going on and this has drained you. Think about your eating habits and what you may be able to change. Plod on with the daily grind but keep an eye out for what takes all your energy.

Saturday 29th

Mercury pops his head back up and upsets your daily routines. Maybe you get delayed on the way to work. Venus helps you to stand up for yourself with manipulative people, and you can do this without the need for aggression or anger. Do not let anyone tell you how to be today.

MARCH
. . . .

Sunday 1st
March begins with a comfortable feeling of satisfaction
with your money and home environment. You have
enough. Thoughts of aspiring to make things better for
yourself are not so important right now. Make the most of
this easy energy as difficulties will come later in the year.

Monday 2nd
The Moon moves into your relationship house and
you just want to talk and talk with a lover or important
person. Conversation flows easily. For you, Sagittarius,
communication is essential in partnerships and can
involve chit-chat or deeper subjects. If you are single,
you will do a lot of thinking.

Tuesday 3rd
Your shadow-side can come out to play now and you
may project your ideals onto another person. Your views
are personal and you cannot make another person
believe the same things. You must learn to value a
person for who they are and not for their points of view.

Wednesday 4th

Mercury is still in his retrograde period and dips his winged heels back into your communications sector. You will find that repeat or return trips are necessary now. There is some unfinished business here. Mercury likes to travel and talk.

Thursday 5th

There is conflict today, between wanting to be nurtured and wanting to parent. You may feel like being a small child again and crave safety and security. Temper tantrums force you to take responsibility for yourself and this can build up resentment. Venus moves into her rulership of your health and duty sector. You will gain more self-worth by getting on with your routines.

Friday 6th

As the Moon moves faster than any other heavenly body, moods can shift and change swiftly. Once more your mood changes and you review your financial situation. You are not taking responsibility for yourself in this area. One minute you are happy, the next you are not.

Saturday 7th

Your heart yearns for travel and higher learning today. This is one of the areas where you excel. Sagittarius is the explorer, the adventurer and the seeker of knowledge. Satisfy your yearning with a good documentary or a great fantasy book and let your mind be taken to distant lands.

Sunday 8th

The planet of love and harmony meets the planet of disruption today. Venus is trying to balance your schedule so that you have time for yourself, but nothing goes right. Meanwhile, the Sun is burning away more of Neptune's illusions and skeletons come out of the family closet.

Monday 9th

Today there is a Full Moon in your career sector. You are a great organiser in the workplace and this is noted. Projects you have been working on for the last six months may now come to fruition and you can expect a reward. Well done.

Tuesday 10th

At last, Mercury turns direct. Travel plans may now be made and contracts signed. You will return to the same issues that Mercury has raised but this time you will get them right. Is there anyone to whom you must apologise? You will be assessing your health today and finding more time for yourself.

Wednesday 11th

Saturn is now at the last degree of your money sector.
It is crucial that you take the next two weeks to
learn hard lessons about your spending and eating.
Friendships and social media groups can help you with
this today. Support groups and forums can offer advice.

Thursday 12th

Solitude beckons and you are soul-searching now.
Travelling to your deepest parts can be painful but there
is gold to be found there. You need to be alert in order
to excavate your soul. Keep a clear head and remain
open to possibilities.

Friday 13th

While you are in the depths of your psyche, know that
there is a lot of Earth energy around today and that
you are held onto safely. When you are ready to
surface and plant your feet back on the ground it will
be solid and stable.

Saturday 14th

The Sun is making helpful connections to Pluto, the
transformer planet. Whatever you found in your darkest
depths can now be brought out into the light and
transformed into something beautiful. This is the value
of soul-searching Sagittarius, finding the light within.
This is the philosopher's stone.

Sunday 15th

The Moon now enters your sign and sector of 'self'.
This is where you show yourself to the world. Your thirst
for adventure and knowledge is what attracts people to
you. Storytelling is a gift you have. Can you make up a
story for someone today? Pass on your learned wisdom.

Monday 16th

Mercury is back in your family sector. Conversations
with family members can be fun and lively. Mercury
also rules laughter and if you use this energy well, your
family life can be a great place to be for the next couple
of weeks. Lead by example with good cheer.

Tuesday 17th

Over the next week, there is unstable energy around
caused by Uranus. This affects your health and duties
sector. Routines may suddenly change and annoy you.
Health concerns will need to be checked, especially blood
pressure. Take responsibility for your own wellbeing. Do
not become a martyr and let your health suffer.

Wednesday 18th

The Moon passes through your money sector and touches Mars, Jupiter and Pluto. This combination means that your emotions can be triggered into aggression easily today. Jupiter will inflate your mood and Pluto will then want to transmute it. This could be an unstable day for you.

Thursday 19th

If you listen and talk with others today, you may learn something to your advantage. Reaching out to people with innovative thinking and a touch of the rebellious can alter your mindset. There is a rebel inside you. What 'outside the box' thinking can you achieve now?

Friday 20th

The spring equinox arrives. This is the astrological New Year, so you can use this as another chance to make good intentions and affirmations. Mars meets your ruler, Jupiter, and you may want to think about new initiatives for bringing in the money. Now is the time to be proactive.

Saturday 21st

Today you will be able to say what is in your heart without fear of rebuke. Family discussions are a little confusing. Members must learn about boundaries and know that even though they have the same gene pool, they are individual and unique. Each has their own path.

Sunday 22nd

Saturn takes a bold step into your communications sector. He will start a train of thought in your head and leave it there for the moment. This will be about how you acquire knowledge and learning. There may be a college course that you are interested in for later.

Monday 23rd

There are two conflicting energies in the air today. The first is a needy and suffocating atmosphere in your family. The second is a powerful and destructive force in your money sector. Something will be torn down or taken away from you now. This is out of your control.

Tuesday 24th

A New Moon in your creative sector gives you yet another chance to make intentions. Anything started now is likely to succeed. For those who are single, this could be a brand-new love affair, or it could be a creative project or your chance to shine your unique light into the world.

Wednesday 25th

Self-expression comes easily now. You will not be afraid to stand up and say your piece. You may be the centre of attention and people will follow your lead, but do not let this go to your head. Be careful not to take on too much. You must learn to delegate.

Thursday 26th

Emotions will be bubbling like a volcano ready to erupt today. The Moon makes uneasy connections to almost every planet in the sky whilst sitting on top of Uranus the disruptor. You will feel divided by your duties and obligations.

Friday 27th

Did you manage to keep your cool? The Moon moves away from the danger zone and peace is restored. That is, unless your inner volcano erupted and you are now wading through the aftermath. If you are dealing with collateral damage today, give yourself some time to get your breath back.

Saturday 28th

Venus in your health and duties sector soothes over any upset caused recently. She connects to Jupiter for added joy. This is a lovely day for connecting to the good things in life. Indulge yourself a little – you deserve it.

Sunday 29th

Partner time comes around again and you enjoy a Sunday afternoon catch up or an evening of light-hearted conversation. Messages and emails can be just as satisfying now. If you are single, positive self-talk can also be good. Learn a few mantras and give yourself a pep talk.

Monday 3oth

Mars is at the last degree of your money sector. You might have to be brutal and cut out unnecessary spending. On the other hand, Mars' energy makes you spontaneous and you could end up breaking the bank. It is your choice how you are going to play this.

Tuesday 3ıst

Mars bumps into Saturn as he enters your communications sector. You are being told off like a naughty schoolchild. Emotionally, you feel like crawling into a safe place and staying there. Isn't this just the reaction of a child who has been caught with their hand in the cookie jar!

APRIL

. . . .

Wednesday 1st
Connections with family and people who nurture you
are good today. There is an easy flow of conversation
and everyone's needs are met. You can be more sensitive
now and feel misunderstood but fear not, this influence
helps to reassure you. A feeling of belonging is strong.

Thursday 2nd
The Moon moves into your travel sector. Here, you
can crave higher education, religion and philosophies
from other cultures. Your search for truth takes you far
away, even if just in your head. Independence is gained
through following your own path. You do not like to be
tied down to obligations today.

Friday 3rd
Venus enters your relationship sector, which is
fantastic news for you. Your love life will become
infused with all that Venus offers. Harmony, beauty
and sensuality are yours to access. Be warned, Venus
will also retrograde here next month, so make the
most of her while she is direct.

Saturday 4th

Chatty Mercury joins Neptune in your family sector. This will be an interesting time when boundaries can merge or be dissolved. The best thing this connection has to offer is a chance to discuss shared dreams and visions. People can become closer by talking to each other under this influence.

Sunday 5th

Jupiter meets Pluto today and their connection will not go unnoticed. At best, jolly Jupiter will help to make a transformation easy, bestowing it with luck. At worst, there will be huge power struggles. This happens in your money and belongings sector. Watch where your spending is going.

Monday 6th

The Moon in your career sector is connecting to the Jupiter/Pluto meet-up. This is a good influence and it is likely that the changes or financial issues will come from work. A promotion or bonus is likely now. Just do not throw it all away on something frivolous.

Tuesday 7th

There can be irritability, tension and anger outbursts today. Upsets to your daily routine will frustrate you. The energy today is volatile and will affect your communications, short trips and daily duties. You want to escape by being with friends and your social groups, but make sure you watch what you say.

Wednesday 8th

A Full Moon in your social sector shows you how important your friends are. You have a large community of friends but only a handful who mean anything. It is time to slim down your friend lists as there may be acquaintances who are not healthy connections for you.

Thursday 9th

This is another volatile day as the Moon makes poor connections to Mars and Uranus, both known for their unpredictability. You want to retreat and have time alone. This is the best time for you to do some soul-searching as the Moon is in your hidden sector of dreams.

Friday 10th

In your solitude, you see the glimmer of a solution to your money problems. This glimmer is also the gold that hides in our darkest places. Jupiter and Pluto together can make this into something wonderful. Will you let them?

Saturday 11th

There is more Fire energy today. You feel uplifted and positive. The Moon has moved into your sign and you can feel more outgoing and sociable. This is also helped by the messenger, Mercury, moving into a Fire sign. He will now give your creativity and self-expression an injection of light-hearted enquiry.

Sunday 12th

Mercury gets a message from Saturn. Communication needs to be kind, honest and helpful. Saturn is like a hippy Zen master and is reminding you to share the love and passion of your creative projects. You may even fall in love at this time. Love is all you need.

Monday 13th

Money continues to worry you. You may not have learned the lessons in being responsible for yourself at an early age and this is now coming back to haunt you. You fear that you will never succeed in your career. It's time to consider whether this is the right career. If not, what might be your true calling?

Tuesday 14th

You feel trapped and sorry for yourself, and the light at the end of the tunnel is nowhere to be seen. Keep calm as this will quickly pass. Use this opportunity to hit pause and just breathe. Think of positives and not negatives right now.

Wednesday 15th

A spotlight shines on your money sector. You must take a good look at what this is illuminating. Do you have too much of something that is not necessary? There is a chance that you are over-exaggerating the importance of some things in your life. What is not bringing you joy any more?

Thursday 16th

Communications and short trips are the themes of the day. This is nice, easy energy and you will be happy to go along with the flow. A partner or loved one may suggest a short outing. A trip to the cinema or a dinner with friends will prove satisfying.

Friday 17th

Family surrounds you today. Think about how you are always there when they need you. Does this work the other way around? Remember that sometimes it is better to say no than to allow yourself to be used. Some give and take is needed in family situations in order to function well.

Saturday 18th

This can be a romantic day for you. You may initiate a plan with a partner and you will both enjoy the sweet conversations you have. Easy communication with partners is crucial for you to maintain a healthy relationship. You can talk until the sun goes down, and into the early hours.

Sunday 19th

The Sun moves into your health and duties sector.
For the next month, you will be wise to look at how your
spending habits affect your ability to get daily routines
done. Eating out is something you enjoy but it is not
helping your bank balance or your figure.

Monday 20th

You get itchy feet today and need to be active. Getting
out and about in nature will help to scratch that itch.
There are many plans forming in your head. A fire rises
in your belly and as yet, you do not know what it means.

Tuesday 21st

Relations between men and women are good today. Your
energy drive and desires are well matched and you can
get what you want. There is a danger of overstepping the
mark, so tread carefully and do not be pushy or forceful.
Take other people's needs into consideration too. Make
sure everyone is happy.

Wednesday 22nd

This is a time to get grounded. The Moon enters your
health and duties sector later today but you feel the
slowing down of energy before this. Get in touch with
your body and do some quiet exercise such as yoga or
meditation. Do nothing strenuous.

Thursday 23rd

A New Moon occurs today. This one is all about setting intentions for grounding yourself. You can do this by starting a new fitness regime or literally planting some seeds. Tending to a garden is like feeding your soul. Review what food you are putting into your body, and why.

Friday 24th

Any intentions set now are likely to be kept. Look at your weekly schedule: is there room for you there? Make time for yourself and let it become a routine. This can be downtime with a book or hobby or making a date with yourself once a week.

Saturday 25th

The Moon moves into your relationship sector and you could have a romantic weekend. However, this will include spending money on new plans and projects. You must keep this under control and find inexpensive ways to have fun with a loved one. Fun and laughter do not have to cost anything.

Sunday 26th

Pluto, the planet of power, control and transformation goes retrograde today. This is the first of the planets in your money sector to do this. The next few months will teach you big lessons on self-control. There will be an unexpected surprise involving health and duties today.

Monday 27th

You are inclined to dig for secrets or uncover something you perceive as unfair. Insecurity rears its ugly head and you need to know why. Getting to the root of a problem unnerves you and you are not sure that you really want the answers now. But would you rather stay in ignorance?

Tuesday 28th

Mercury is now in your health and duties sector. He can add wings to your routine and can lift up areas that you think are dull or stuck. A little research and fact-finding about niggling health issues would be good now. Mercury lends you his detective skills.

Wednesday 29th

Emotionally you still feel that you want to hide or be cared for. Sometimes, other people's feelings are too intense for you to cope with. You must learn to express your own deepest feelings in order to appreciate where other people are coming from.

Thursday 30th

The Moon enters your travel sector now. Long-distance journeys attract you, as does higher education. Consider whether you are using these as a distraction from your emotional life. Running away does not solve anything, but it can help to put your priorities into perspective.

MAY

. . . .

Friday 1st
What an unstable day this is! Expect delays and
disruptions with all kinds of travel. This will be
frustrating but you must find a way to accept things that
are beyond your control. On top of this, Mercury meets
Uranus and you will see harsh arguments or genius
thinking in your daily routines.

Saturday 2nd
Today the Moon shifts into your work sector but as it is
the weekend you may find that you are spending time on
paperwork in the home. De-clutter a messy spot of bills.
Alternatively, you may be putting your CD collection or
books in alphabetical order.

Sunday 3rd
This is an orderly day for you. Easy energy from the
Moon helps you to think about change. Writing down
plans for getting finances straight will give you more
incentive and help clarify a few issues. Seek advice
from wise counsellors or advisors and take what they
say on board.

Monday 4th

Friendships and social groups can offer you the help
you need right now. Mercury is consumed by the Sun
and this can make you feel overwhelmed with ideas. He
will be receiving new information but for now, turn to
people in the wider world. Social media groups will
be useful.

Tuesday 5th

The point of destiny changes signs and will spend the
next eighteen months in your relationship sector. This
will enhance your need for someone to partner with.
However, this person will need to be on your intellectual
level and be able to talk all through the night with you.

Wednesday 6th

The Moon dives into the deepest part of your chart where
you find yourself seeking solitude and personal truths.
Keep an open mind and stay positive. Why not indulge in
good books or TV where you may find a path to follow.

Thursday 7th

A super intense Full Moon happens today in your dream
sector. Whilst you are mining for gold in the deepest
level of your psyche, the Moon shines on something in
a dark corner. Dare you pick it up? Consider the last six
months in this area; what have you dug up so far?

Friday 8th

A breath of fresh air hits you as you surface to find the
Moon in your sign. You like to stride out again after
being in the Underworld. Re-energised and motivated,
you face the world running. Do you want to share
something with the world now?

Saturday 9th

Mercury is getting to grips with his new mission. He
connects to Pluto in your money sector and is making
you see that it is possible to transform lead into gold.
You are overlooking a talent that you feel is worthless.
It can be of great use to you now.

Sunday 10th

Another connection is made by Mercury. This time, he
sees Jupiter, another of the planets in your money sector.
Jupiter can represent the law, authorities or God. You
realise that the help you need may be of a legal nature.
This is a great insight Sagittarius. Seek financial advice.

Monday 11th

The planet of karma, Saturn, now turns retrograde.
He does this in your communications sector but will
retreat and join other planets in your money sector.
This is a time of harsh lessons regarding finances,
possessions and self-worth. You will learn not to form
emotional attachments to objects.

Tuesday 12th

Your relationships are about to get noisy! Mercury
enters a sign he rules and will be having a party.
Exchanging ideas, philosophies and ethics with a
partner will become very important. Conversation is the
key to a lively relationship for you. Make the most of
Mercury's stay here.

Wednesday 13th

Just as you get more talkative with your partner,
Venus has to go and upset the status quo by turning
retrograde. This could mean that the communication
you have now will be more on the defensive side.
Disputes between lovers are more likely. This will be a
testing time for relationships.

Thursday 14th

Mars drove his chariot into your family sector whilst
Venus was making her point. His placement here can
help to divert any unwanted interactions with partners.
Keeping your energy and drive focused on family
matters can help avoid upsets with partners. Show
family how focused you can be.

Friday 15th

Your emotions join your will in your family sector now. There could be someone who is throwing their weight around and causing upset. Meanwhile, Jupiter joins the army of retrogrades in your money sector. This may mean that it takes longer to sort out legalities regarding finances.

Saturday 16th

You are starting to feel what this Venus retrograde is going to bring up for you. A sensitive Moon is squaring off with the planet of love and harmony. This could be that you are struggling to divide your time between the demands of your lover and those of your family.

Sunday 17th

Deciding to put your all into an art project could save the day. This sector also deals with love affairs so it may be that you make more effort in your relationship. You get a helping hand from the Sun who gives you more control over your finances and home life.

Monday 18th

Today you are more assertive and speak your mind. This too involves your love life but is an easy energy and nothing to worry about. Talking with a partner about new plans can help to inject new life into a part of your relationship that is struggling.

Tuesday 19th

Another smooth day in your relationships as the Moon and Venus are having a lady's night. Love and harmony can be restored for a short while. One partner may try to get their own way but it is soon forgotten about. Try not to beat about the bush, be open and honest.

Wednesday 20th

The Moon enters your daily routines sector. This helps to ground you in the nine to five and bring you back down to earth for a while. The Sun now makes its way into your relationships sector and can help to heat things up, although this can go both ways.

Thursday 21st

Getting back in touch with your own body through yoga, meditation or walks in nature will go a long way today. A date night with yourself or a partner can be sensual and help to re-connect you. Good food and a little luxury can absorb any tension you have been feeling.

Friday 22nd

Today there is a New Moon in your relationships sector. You can re-commit to your partner or, if necessary, bring something to a loving end. Venus retrogrades can often imply break-ups or someone from the past returning. Try to be as compassionate as you can.

Saturday 23rd

Mars is getting tired. You have a lot of pressure from family now and it is hard to do the right thing by everyone. Keep plodding on and find the spiritual warrior in you. Drive your chariot onwards with a destination in mind. Let that destination be fairness for all around you.

Sunday 24th

The Moon hits the point of destiny which is now in your relationships sector. You may be pulled to a distant point in the future. The best thing to do today is to be present in the here and now. Appreciate what is, and not what might be.

Monday 25th

Today you will be feeling over-sensitive and want to hide away. This is normal for you when the Moon enters your sex, death and rebirth sector but with everything else going on, you are feeling it more. You do not want to discuss the deeper subjects. You just need the safety of what is familiar.

Tuesday 26th

Issues of control arrive today to attempt to get you out of your shell. It is not easy for you to speak about your feelings now. Someone is pressuring you and trying to get you to open up and this may upset you. Stay safe today.

Wednesday 27th

Along comes the time of the month when you just want to get away. If you are lucky enough to do this then do it. Some fresh air and new places will do you good. If you are trapped, you will be like a caged lion and pace the floor all day.

Thursday 28th

Mercury leaves your relationship sector. There is no more talking to be done. He now infiltrates your comfort zones and asks questions about yourself. There is one good question he asks you, do you have money tied up with a certain someone? Do you need to sort this out now?

Friday 29th

Setting your mind to your career will benefit you today. You need to take your thoughts away from troubles and strife. Diving headlong into overdue tasks and deadlines can land you back in the physical world of everyday life. You will be glad of the distraction.

Saturday 30th

What is building for you since the New Moon? Can you feel a shift within your relationships or family matters? If possible, stick with the paperwork today as tension is rising and you feel edgy. Occupy yourself with mundane duties or simply some time alone to read a book.

Sunday 31st

You are feeling more sociable now and do not want to waste any more of your weekend. Get out with friends today. Social interactions can help you feel less alone. You may even learn that other people are having a hard time too. Safety is in numbers today Sagittarius.

JUNE

....

Monday 1st

The heavyweight planets are getting you down today.
Time spent with support groups and close friendships
can help to shed some of this load. You may learn
something new now and want to sit and ruminate on
it before forming an opinion. Money matters will also
cause some distress.

Tuesday 2nd

Your dreams sector is where you will be hiding today.
Solitude is what you crave but this is an avoidance
tactic. Watch how you react and respond to the darkness
of your own being. Make sure that it is not your own
feelings that you are hiding from.

Wednesday 3rd

Venus is now in the heart of the Sun and still in
retrograde. Relationships are in a hot spot and you may
be facing a dilemma. The Moon is also opposite volatile
Uranus which adds to the unpredictability of the day.
This could be a tough day in love Sagittarius.

Thursday 4th

As the Moon moves into your sign, you get fired up and
want more action. However, as this is the Moon, this
will be expressed internally. Families can be the cause
of some unrest today. Your close relationships will be
at odds with your family obligations. You feel pulled in
both directions.

Friday 5th

Today is your Full Moon. You can get some insight
or revelations about how you go after your goals
and intentions. What have you learned in the last six
months? The need to do things your way and to explore
the wider world is strong now. Travel is important to you.

Saturday 6th

Are you beating yourself up for missing out on
opportunities? Did you say no to something because of
other obligations? This comes back to haunt you now.
You realise that others hold you back from your truth-
seeking adventures and exploration.

Sunday 7th

Resentment kicks in and you worry about finances
again. You have big plans but do not have the money to
carry them out. Fear not, your time will come. This is a
test of your patience and will be a valuable lesson on
how to manage your resources.

Monday 8th

The Moon passes the planets currently blocking your progress in your money and possessions sector. You must adapt to this time of the month or it will drag you down. Use this time to pause, reflect and ask for help if needed. Paternal and authority figures will be of use to you.

Tuesday 9th

A meeting with someone who is a great teacher to you is possible today. Short trips may be a nuisance but hold value. Communication of all sorts is favoured now. Listen to someone who may have a radical solution for you. Do not discard any advice today, take it on board.

Wednesday 10th

There will be some family issues today. Who is the sacrificial lamb in the tribe, Sagittarius? Again, there is tension between family and partners. This is not easy energy and you can be either disillusioned or have the wool pulled over your eyes. Maybe you are that lamb or scapegoat.

Thursday 11th

At the moment, despite the feeling of being used, family is where you need to be. This is possibly a distraction from dealing with any problems in your personal relationships. Your roots and family bonds are very important to you. Family will always be there for you when others aren't.

Friday 12th

The theme of family versus partners continues today as the Moon is squaring off to Venus. Your desires are to be with your partner, but you crave the comfort and security of your family. Mothers can be an enormous comfort or a thorn in your side today Sagittarius.

Saturday 13th

The Moon makes some roller-coaster connections in your family sector today. First, she hits Mars and tempers can rise. Next, she comes across Neptune who can throw a blanket of floaty energy over the tension. Moods come and go quickly. This can briefly unsettle you but it will not last long.

Sunday 14th

Today brings a welcome break from recent disturbances.
There is tension in the air but it is the best kind.
Your passion for creative projects can be re-ignited.
Speaking your truth comes easier and you can feel more
optimistic now. Something has ended in order to make
way for the new.

Monday 15th

Mercury is flying around in your sex, death and rebirth
sector. You can be very protective of your deepest,
darkest secrets here. He is about to go retrograde so
the warning applies now: back up devices, double
check travel plans and play nice! Shared finances need
checking now too.

Tuesday 16th

You put your mind to mundane activities today. Cooking
and eating can bring pleasure. You are dependable when
it comes to getting your daily routine done and others
thank you for it. A day like today goes a long way to
bringing your emotions back down to earth.

Wednesday 17th

Saturn has now returned to the very beginning of your
communications sector. He will retrace his steps further
into your money sector too. Today he is asking if you have
overlooked an important meeting or phone call. Is there
someone you were meaning to get back to and did not?

Thursday 18th

Mercury retrograde begins. For you Sagittarius, this is your chance to review and assess what has been going on for you in the sector which deals with intimacy, shared finances, beginnings and endings. You may have already learned a lot but now is the time to assimilate those lessons and re-evaluate their worth.

Friday 19th

Today the Sun meets the point of destiny in Gemini for the first time. This deals with your relationships with partners and the one you have with yourself. This can illuminate areas that need work in order to visualise and manifest a future of honest communication. Be true to yourself.

Saturday 20th

There is great energy from Mars and Jupiter in your family sector. Think of a spiritual warrior mixed with Santa Claus. Mars will be sticking up for the underdog whilst Jupiter bestows his gifts. Jupiter's retrograde gifts are lessons in giving and not receiving. This is family pull-together time.

Sunday 21st

Today is the Summer Solstice but with a twist. The day of longest light has a shadow thrown over it with a solar eclipse. You make others think that you are showing your feelings, being open and vulnerable, but you are not. This is quite possibly your greatest fear.

Monday 22nd

With the Moon in Cancer and meeting up with Mercury in retrograde, you feel exposed today. What the eclipse brought up is known only to you, but Mercury will root it out and you could confide in someone. This will leave you regretting that you did so Sagittarius.

Tuesday 23rd

Yet another planet goes retrograde today. Neptune, the planet of dreams, illusions and sacrifices turns around in your family sector. This can make everything very foggy and you will be unsure of a lot of things now. Skeletons will come out of the family closet to be healed once and for all.

Wednesday 24th

You have a hard time separating yourself from family members now. Your instinct is to point out how educated and travelled you are but this will not do you any favours. Being pushy and showing off will set you apart from people more than you would like.

Thursday 25th

One small saving grace for today is that the Venus retrograde is over. What has left your life during the last forty days? Have you had anyone you thought was long gone return? A tough time of break-ups and make-ups is now over but the effects will be long-lasting or even final.

Friday 26th

Mars in your family sector does not know whether he is coming or going. You will feel this as an impulse to leave versus an obligation to stay. People are relying on you but what for? Make sure that their reasons are not selfish and if so, be free to leave.

Saturday 27th

Staying with Mars energy today and the need to finish something up regarding families, mothers and ancestry. Mars is on the critical last degree and is asking you to think hard about bringing something to completion before he moves into his own sign and picks up the pace again.

Sunday 28th

Mars lands in his own sign and in your creativity sector. This is also the area where you can laugh and play. Expressing your unique self is possible now. Mars will give you the energy you need to get on with artistic projects that you may have put to one side.

Monday 29th

The Moon is in your social sector but making an uneasy connection to the planets in your money sector. It looks like you will be saying no to a lot of plans made by your social groups. You simply cannot afford this right now. Regrettably, you must miss out.

Tuesday 30th

Today you just want to be alone and switch off from the world. You feel sorry for yourself. There will be control issues with leaders, religion or the law today. Pluto, who deals with power and transformation, meets up with massive Jupiter who makes everything bigger and they are both retrograde.

JULY
. . . .

Wednesday 1st
Mercury is back in the heat of the Sun in your relationship sector. You should receive some enlightenment today about recent events with the two retrogrades covering this area. Something that was confusing will now be made clear. You will get an 'aha!' moment.

Thursday 2nd
As the Moon enters your own sign you feel more optimistic and outgoing. Adventures call you, even if that means getting out of your pyjamas and going to the shop. On a larger scale, your confidence could be hiding a vulnerability and you may get offended easily today.

Friday 3rd
Try not to take your good spirits for granted. Someone may come along and spoil your mood. A flippant comment by an associate may mean nothing but you are sensitive now and can easily take things the wrong way. Be your usual outgoing self and ride the waves of the day.

Saturday 4th

Your resources will be foremost in your mind for the next couple of days. This is an unfortunate theme for this year Sagittarius. Saturn has moved back into this sector indicating that you need help and advice from professionals. He has come back to sort things out.

Sunday 5th

A Full Moon and lunar eclipse in your money sector make you anxious today. The illumination shows what has been happening for you regarding your resources this year. You may get an idea of how to proceed now. The eclipse will throw a shadow over an area that needs investigating.

Monday 6th

Today you may find yourself making short trips or writing a lot of messages. The Moon is making a lovely connection to Venus in your relationship sector. This means that if you have making up to do, now is a good time. Restoring harmony with a partner is favoured.

Tuesday 7th

Communication is the key to any good relationship. You know this more than anyone Sagittarius. Today is filled with mental energy but you must be subtle and kind if you are trying to reconcile your relationship. Words can hurt and you do not need any more of that, do you?

Wednesday 8th

There is a stand-off today between retrograde Mercury and Mars in his own sign. This almost always indicates accidents, travel delays and aggression. You could be rash and impulsive today. Think before you speak and keep alert when travelling today Sagittarius. Try not to upset anyone in the family.

Thursday 9th

Maybe your attempts to restore balance in a personal relationship have not worked. Do not push this issue any further today Sagittarius. Once more the Moon and Venus have fallen out and this will cause tension between family and lovers. You must choose where best to invest your energy today.

Friday 10th

Sometimes you can feel like whatever you do is just not good enough. Today is one of those days. Your empathic qualities are stretched to the limits and you now need to put boundaries in place and say "NO". You are willing to help those in need but must put yourself first at times.

Saturday 11th

As the Moon shifts, you are more able to express yourself. People will listen to you now. This is also a good phase for creative projects and expressing yourself in that way. The energy is more focused and whatever you do will be a source of satisfaction to you.

Sunday 12th

Mercury turns direct and you can breathe again. It is now safe to think about any offers or contracts you were offered recently. Travel plans may now be made without the planetary influence of disruption. The Sun connects to Neptune and helps to clear some fog now.

Monday 13th

The best thing you can do for the next couple of days is to get your head down and plod on with your daily routines. Mundane activities like cooking can give you more pleasure than you think at this time. Satisfaction comes from knowing that chores are done with nothing outstanding.

Tuesday 14th

The Sun in your sector of sex, death and rebirth is shining its light on Jupiter in your money sector. You may get a little financial reprieve or a helping hand. Something could shock or surprise you today. Try cooking up a new recipe and make your taste buds tingle.

Wednesday 15th

The Sun now opposes Pluto. This may well manifest in seeing a solution to a problem with your resources. Pluto likes to transform things. He also likes power and control. You may get the chance to make a change for the better in your home or finances. You regain control.

Thursday 16th

Today you can be broody and moody about recent events with a loved one. If you are single, this is the time to look at the connections that you have with people. This can be business or intimate relationships. Look at those that no longer serve you and those that do.

Friday 17th

The Moon and Venus are friends again. They sit in your relationship sector and discuss what it is that you want from partnerships. Listen well to what comes up for you. Old relating habits are hard to change but this is now necessary for healthy, balanced partnerships of all kinds.

Saturday 18th

Today you just know that something has come to an end. Try to see the positives in this. There will be more room for something new to come into your life which can be more fulfilling. Do not lie to yourself about this and do not hide from your own feelings.

Sunday 19th

The Moon meets Mercury fresh from his recent retrograde. You will be having a head and heart discussion with yourself. Mercury wants to know what you have learned. He will be asking deep questions which you may not like but listen well because the head is more rational than the heart.

Monday 20th

There is a New Moon today in your sex, death and rebirth sector. This area is concerned with the mysteries of the cycles of life. Now is your chance to make yourself vulnerable and begin to show your deepest feelings. No more hiding, Sagittarius.

Tuesday 21st

Your travel sector is highlighted now and you yearn to get away. Life is not big enough for you and you can sometimes feel trapped by obligations. Is this a reaction to being vulnerable? Ensure that this is not an ego trip. How you are perceived by others, is not who you really are.

Wednesday 22nd

The Sun now follows the Moon into your travel sector
and will fill you up with Fire energy. This suits you,
being a Fire sign. You can now be more courageous and
step outside your comfort zone. Higher education and
new philosophies attract you. The world is waiting.

Thursday 23rd

Mercury is wandering through your sex, death and
rebirth sector and is uncovering something unusual
now. This may be a skill or a talent you did not know
you had. He will find a topic that piques his interest and
drag it up from your subconscious to examine its worth.

Friday 24th

The workplace will have you thinking about how you
serve others today. You are a happy worker and get
the job done without complaints but today you may
find that sacrifices are made that are not in your best
interests. This is a case of blurred boundaries again.

Saturday 25th

The weekend brings you a Moon in your social sector. Get
out and have a good time with your friends. Social media
connections can be fun today. Your need to connect with
the wider world can be satisfied by online contact, groups
and pages of interest. Have a sociable Saturday.

Sunday 26th

Be careful that someone does not get too close for comfort today. There is a danger that people who you connect with over social media think they know the real you. They think that this allows them certain liberties when interacting with you. Is your social media profile a pretence?

Monday 27th

This can be a difficult day. There are some tense connections between planets which can mean that arguments, violence and manipulation can occur today. This will involve your love life and family. You want nothing to do with any of it and try to retreat. You must face this Sagittarius.

Tuesday 28th

You can have a problem with boundaries again today. This is a big lesson for you. Letting anyone and everyone into your life is not healthy and gives you an unreal perspective on who is really there for you. Free yourself from energy vampires. Stop trying to save everyone.

Wednesday 29th

The Moon enters your sign but you are tired. This phase usually gives you more enthusiasm but today you feel flat. This may be a good time to opt out and take some time to do what interests you. Pick up a book you had forgotten about and escape today.

Thursday 30th

Mercury is still rummaging around in your psyche. There is more work to be done here. Today he wants you to consider how father figures have affected you. Men in authority have left something in your deeper unconscious and can be the root of the way you handle responsibility.

Friday 31st

Now that Mercury is dragging things up regarding paternal and maternal figures you can begin to work out why you mismanage your resources. Listen carefully to what is being revealed and prepare to make changes. This tough patch is meant to get to the bottom of your conditioning around money.

AUGUST
....

Saturday 1st
There is an interesting opposition between Mercury and
Pluto today. They are in sectors which deal with mothers
and fathers, income and resources. Mercury is telling
Pluto what he has found in your psyche and Pluto is
getting ready to transform this for you. Nurturing and
responsibility also feature.

Sunday 2nd
People may be throwing their weight around today. This
could be you Sagittarius. Your need to be an individual
with lofty aspirations might grate on someone now.
Expect some aggravation to come from your health and
duties sector. There may be tantrums after which you
run away. This will not make you look good.

Monday 3rd
A Full Moon in your communication sector will show
you what is worth your breath. You could be raising a
revolution with the things you speak about and share.
Unusual or unfair topics make you speak out but please
check your sources before you do. Watch out for fake news.

Tuesday 4th

Mars is getting a telling off from Jupiter today. Your creative pursuits have had a fantastic boost while Mars has been hanging around but has this added to your spending? You may find that passion or speaking your mind comes with a cost that right now, you just cannot afford.

Wednesday 5th

The Moon enters your family sector and gives you an easy time with loved ones. You want to feel a part of the tribe. Home comforts drag you back to the fold and immerse you in the nurturing love that you need. A brief interlude from all the tension.

Thursday 6th

Venus, who is still in your relationship sector, meets the point of fate today. Look ahead with her. Can you see a future where love, beauty and harmony in your relationships are possible? Use this moment to make a wish for all that you desire in a loving partnership.

Friday 7th

Venus steps into your sex, death and rebirth sector. Home is where the heart is but sex is where the passion is. You can have a hard time establishing what an intimate connection means for you. Venus will help you to work with your deepest desires while she is here.

Saturday 8th

An active fiery Moon is connecting to Mercury who is now in your travel sector. You will be thinking about getting away under this influence. Mercury loves to travel and he will inspire you with new ideas. New places and new cultures will get you excited now. Learn all you can.

Sunday 9th

Your outgoing mood is stopped in its tracks today by an influence from the heavy planets in your money sector. You must be realistic about any new plans or projects. Find a way to afford to continue with your passionate projects which does not cost so much.

Monday 10th

When the Moon enters your health and duties sector, it comes across unstable Uranus. You can be temperamental at these times. This is a reminder to get a health check-up as blood pressure could be building. Look at what you are eating too, is it healthy as well as tasty?

Tuesday 11th

The daily grind might get you down today. You can
feel trapped by your obligations and any plans to get
away may seem thwarted. This is a phase that will pass
quickly. Sit with it Sagittarius, all is not as hopeless as it
may seem. Do your jobs and think again tomorrow.

Wednesday 12th

Do you fancy a midweek treat with a partner? Connect
with someone in a meaningful way today Sagittarius.
Conversation can flow over a dinner date. If you are
single, date yourself with a delicious take out and a good
book or TV show. Online dating can be fun.

Thursday 13th

Something is about to erupt today. Mars and Pluto are
squaring off in your creative and money sectors. Mars
will destroy something and leave new ground to build
anew. Pluto will try to transform rather than destroy.
You might think about buying and selling. This could be
beneficial to you now.

Friday 14th

You might find the Mars and Pluto connection gets out
of hand today. Tempers can flare and manipulation is
possible. See if you can use this powerful, volatile energy
to create some messy art or angry poetry. Alternatively,
this energy could imply falling in love in a dramatic way.

Saturday 15th

Venus and the Moon meet up again, this time in your sex, death and rebirth sector. You are not altogether comfortable being open and exposed and would rather keep your deepest feelings to yourself. Venus can coax you with her sweet voice. Choose wisely who you share secrets with today.

Sunday 16th

Uranus joins the outer planets in retrograde now. This can be a disruptive time in your health and duties sector and you may experience burn-out. Make sure that there is enough time in the day for you to do everything you have to do and time left over for things you want to do.

Monday 17th

The Moon heads into your travel sector again. You might be pacing the floor like a caged lion now. There is pent-up frustration within you and your answer is to run away from it all. Can you indulge your sense of escape by watching documentaries?

Tuesday 18th

A New Moon occurs in your travel sector. This Moon will be rather self-centred and you will feel that your needs are not being met. This is your opportunity to set intentions for yourself. Make plans and plant thought seeds regarding where you would like to travel to in the near future.

Wednesday 19th

Today you have a chance to look into the future and back at the past. The Sun is in your travel sector and holding both points for you to consider. Where have you enjoyed going? Where would you like to go? Use this time to plant those intentions firmly.

Thursday 20th

Mercury has finished up in your travel sector and is now at work with you. The messenger will be busy collecting information, doing your filing and researching new projects. You could be over-worked now but you will sail through it with the help of the winged one in his own sign.

Friday 21st

It is the weekend and you are in the mood for some fun with friends. This is the one area of your life which seems to be more balanced. You have a handful of faithful friends and an army of online friends. You have a great support team.

Saturday 22nd

The Sun now follows Mercury and lights up your career sector. If you play your cards right this powerful combination can mean that your efforts and efficiency at work will not go unnoticed. Finish up the summer months with a good attitude towards your work and rewards will come.

Sunday 23rd

Have a Sunday alone Sagittarius. Solitude is not the same as loneliness and can bring a deep thinker like you many benefits. Switch off from the hustle and bustle and listen to your inner voice. You can get your best thinking done at these times if you are in the mood.

Monday 24th

Forward moving Mars is now held back by Saturn. Have you perhaps pushed too far into something new? You may have overstepped a boundary and did not realise it. Did you expect too much from someone who failed to keep up with you? Ensure that you are not too demanding now.

Tuesday 25th

The Moon enters your sign today and you can feel good but more tired than usual. You may get a bit of luck today with your financial situation as Venus, who rules money is facing Jupiter who rules luck. He is retrograde but Venus can sweet-talk him.

Wednesday 26th

You may well have the gift of the gab today and can persuade the boss to give you a raise. Mercury is dominating your workplace. There could be laughter or gossip. Something shocking may be revealed by accident. Do not partake in a game of Chinese whispers, Sagittarius.

Thursday 27th

Today has a floaty, dreamy feel to it. You and someone
you are intimate with are merging into each other. Could
this be the beginning of a love affair? Venus is in your
sector where you explore the depths and Neptune is in
the deepest ocean. These two are connecting nicely now.

Friday 28th

The Moon is in contact with Uranus which means
that you may have a surprise, nice or nasty with your
finances. There could be a shake-up where you will see a
resolution in a different light. A new perspective can be
found now if you know where to look.

Saturday 29th

There is very mixed energy today. This will feel very
weird and unsettle you. The Moon is making a lot of
good and bad connections. As it is a weekend, maybe
you should stay home and watch some TV or read a
book until this phase passes.

Sunday 30th

Communications are favourable today. You can persuade
or coerce and get what you want. Mercury is speaking
out from your work sector and putting all his dreams out
there for people to hear. You have a magic moment and
can manifest your goals now; however unreachable they
may seem.

Monday 31st

Mars is close to finishing up in your creative sector.
Over the next few days, make sure that art projects
are completed. If you have fallen for someone during
his stay here, this initial phase can be planted in solid
ground when Mars moves into the next sign and builds
foundations. Lucky you, Sagittarius.

SEPTEMBER

. . . .

Tuesday 1st

A helpful connection between Mercury and Pluto means
that the workplace and your resources are highlighted.
The messenger is using information from your job and
delivering it to the right place to help with your financial
problems. Is there something you can resurrect to bring
in more money?

Wednesday 2nd

Today there is a Full Moon in your family sector. This
is a deeply emotional Moon and you could find a lot of
issues from the past are now coming up to be healed.
Mothers and fathers are indicated by a Venus and Saturn
opposition in signs connected to parental roles.

Thursday 3rd

Mercury is still carrying messages from your workplace.
This time, he delivers to Saturn. Listen out for advice
regarding responsibility and discipline. Saturn also deals
with karma so the problems you are facing now could be
consequences from past actions. Your mood lifts a little
after the heavy Full Moon.

Friday 4th

Today you may see issues brought up by the Full Moon.
Venus and Mars are squaring off. Venus takes on a
motherly role while Mars is still strong in your creative
sector. Expressing yourself to women can be difficult
today. Venus has an ally in Mercury to lend her
wilful words.

Saturday 5th

Having delivered his messages to your troubled
resources sector, Mercury flies into your social sector
and will now have some fun. Expect a lot of socialising
now. You may be called upon to act as a mediator and
bring balance and harmony to friendship. You may
moderate online forums and interest groups.

Sunday 6th

Venus also shifts signs now. She glides into your travel
sector. Here she will bring you more courage and
determination to be yourself. Venus also rules food and you
could find that you will be dining out more than usual now.
Sampling exotic food will satisfy your urge to travel.

Monday 7th

Back to the working week and it is possible that you are
not feeling well. The Moon makes her monthly visit to
your health and duties sector. This is the area of your life
which can drain you. Check in with your body now and
see what it is lacking.

Tuesday 8th

Today you want to connect. You think about how your family relationships may have had an impact on how you choose a partner. The need for conversation and shared dreams is strong today. Your sense of duty and responsibility is divided between family and lovers. This can make you resentful.

Wednesday 9th

A happier day today as the Sun in your career sector sends its rays towards Jupiter who is the joyful planet. This influence fills your heart with courage and your working day benefits. Travel plans may be discussed with a partner or you may choose to be brave and travel alone.

Thursday 10th

Mars now turns retrograde in your creative sector. Just as he was about to move on he retraces his steps with a sulk. The good thing is that he is still in his rulership. Your creative expression may be halted but not abandoned. Love affairs may also be on hold.

Friday 11th

Today you will not want to come out of your shell. You are being asked to show your feelings on deep subjects and get rather defensive. A Sun and Neptune opposition burns away some illusions or masks concerning family issues and you are not in the mood to deal with them.

Saturday 12th

You are still in a dark mood and what makes it worse
is that you have to face some money issues. There are
solutions being offered but you feel overwhelmed. It
is best that you have a Saturday to yourself and enjoy
comfort foods or a good book.

Sunday 13th

A piece of good news today is that Jupiter now turns
direct. This will feel like a massive release of pressure
that was building in your money and resource sector. The
Moon dips into your travel sector and you feel more like
yourself again. However, take baby steps today, take it easy.

Monday 14th

Moon and Venus join together and help you to love
being yourself again. Your individuality can sometimes
frighten even you. A brave Venus gives you the strength
needed to return to your brilliant authentic self. There
is no need to compromise Sagittarius, be yourself and
nobody else.

Tuesday 15th

At work, you contemplate how you might advance your
career. You look back at what you enjoyed and worked
hard for in the past. How might you bring that into the
current time and build a future with it? There may be
some upset in your routine today. Check your health.

Wednesday 16th

When the Moon is in your career sector you are efficient and methodical. Today you will be contemplating how much you do for other people. You do not mind this but you question whether others are learning from you or using you. You are pulled between what you want to do and have to do.

Thursday 17th

A New Moon in your career sector gives you the chance to do something about your recent thinking. Make mini-resolutions to stop being a martyr or the workhorse in the office. There are some responsibilities that no longer need your attention and you can delegate to others now.

Friday 18th

You start the weekend with the need to be with friends. However, you have some guilt about spending money. Do not worry Sagittarius, be mindful of your spending habits and you can still have a good time without going overboard. Allow yourself a little bit of fun today.

Saturday 19th

Actions and emotions are not in sync today. Your social sector is bubbling with activities you want to be involved in but your energy is lacking. You are still having concerns about money and this is preventing you from joining in with things. Try to balance this today.

Sunday 20th

The Moon in your dreams and private sector has made you feel like retreating now. You can be quite down and drift off into the murky waters of your unconscious. This can stir up some deep emotions that you prefer to keep to yourself. You would rather not deal with your shadow today.

Monday 21st

The Moon shifts and enters your own sign. You can be boisterous now but this is only a mask to hide how you really feel. People rely on you to be the outgoing one and lead them into unknown territory. Little do they know what is going on in your head.

Tuesday 22nd

The Sun moves into your social sector for the next month. This influence will uplift your friendship groups and bring more people with the same interests into your circle. Balancing time with close friends and time with other associates comes easily now. You will be a social butterfly.

Wednesday 23rd

Mercury is still in your social sector making new contacts and having great conversations every day. Today he gets a lesson from Saturn concerning boundaries. Are you sure that you are connecting with the right people? Many friends do not mean that all of them are good for you.

Thursday 24th

There may be arguments or confrontations in your social circle today Sagittarius. Mercury is opposite Mars and this connection makes conversations volatile and aggressive. Refrain from being a keyboard warrior and being controversial on social media. Being almost anonymous online does not give you the right to hit and run.

Friday 25th

Today can bring a mixed bag of emotions Sagittarius. The Moon will pass over all of the planets in your money sector. First, you will feel great, then you will feel the heaviness of Pluto and Saturn. Stick with it, this is a quickly passing phase, do not act on it.

Saturday 26th

The Moon is now in your communications sector and gives you some relief. You love to talk and you seek like-minded people with which to discuss your interests. Be careful not to become misinformed and in turn mislead those you communicate with. Do your research and check all facts.

Sunday 27th

Mercury is now flying around in your deepest subconscious. Right now he is looking to connect with a spiritual source. He is looking for a divine being, God or something else outside himself to commune with. Your search for spiritual enlightenment heightens with Mercury here. Prayer and meditation are useful.

Monday 28th

Today has a family theme but not your direct family.
You may be thinking about your ancestry. Stories and
information from generations past attract you and you
may go searching for ancestors in order to make more
sense of who you are. Belonging is important to you now.

Tuesday 29th

You can breathe another sigh of relief today as Saturn
goes direct in your money sector. If you have learned
the lessons of self-discipline and responsibility during
his retrograde period, you will see the way forward. If
you have still to learn them, then Saturn as the planet of
karma will return.

Wednesday 30th

Mars is squaring off to Saturn today. You can feel
irritable today and possibly resentful. This energy is
like a naughty schoolchild being told off by the teacher.
Saturn now guides you step by step through the last part
of your money sector. Listen and learn.

OCTOBER

. . . .

Thursday 1st

October begins with a Full Moon in your creative sector.
What you have been working on and building may well
come to fruition now. This will illuminate how strong
and determined you have been all year. Love affairs
may come back into the light. Keep up with the self-
expression, you are doing well.

Friday 2nd

Venus now enters your career sector and will infuse the
workplace with love and harmony. As she is also the ruler
of money, this will give your finances a boost. You may
also find that your willingness to serve is at peace with
your own agendas now. Enjoy Venus' influence here.

Saturday 3rd

The Moon enters your sector of health and duty. She
makes a helpful connection to Venus and all the Venus
issues of love, harmony, peace and money will affect your
daily schedule. You may take some time for yourself now
and not feel guilty about it.

Sunday 4th

Today will bring up a potentially difficult situation. The Moon sits on top of Uranus the disruptor and is also opposite motormouth Mercury in your deep, hidden parts. Mercury may find something that makes you very uncomfortable. This has come up for healing now Sagittarius, do not be afraid of your own shadow.

Monday 5th

Breathe! Pluto is direct. He is the last of the planets blocking your progress with money to go forward again. You will notice that things in this area will pick up enormously now. The passing Moon in your duties sector gives her blessing to all three and you are more emotionally stable.

Tuesday 6th

You can have a welcome break today and spend time with a lover or your inner lover. Conversations are stimulating and upbeat now that the heavyweights are facing forward. This influence can make you laugh and get your joy for life back again. Simply have light-hearted connections today.

Wednesday 7th

There is a chance that someone may knock you off your happy place today. This could be more stuff from your subconscious rising up and making itself known. You must learn that these moments are happening for you to heal your wounds and let your shadow see the light.

Thursday 8th

The Moon drifts into your sex, death and rebirth sector.
What have you learned regarding hiding your feelings?
You could feel exposed today as a lover or partner wants
to probe deeper than you would like. Defence is not
necessary if you can just learn to trust and open up.

Friday 9th

Retrograde Mars is sulking in your creative sector. There
may be issues of control now. Someone could be acting
out on you and trying to push an issue that they feel is
important. Use your communication skills to control the
situation. Do not manipulate. Stay calm and objective.

Saturday 10th

The Moon sits opposite your money sector. You might
be thinking about finances that you share with another
person. Investments seem like a good idea but you may
not want to indulge now that you have some control
back with your money and resources. Put this away for
another time.

Sunday 11th

When the Moon enters your travel sector, you usually
feel brave and adventurous. Today she makes unhappy
connections which could rock your boat. You can be
knocked off a pedestal now and feel the bruises on your
ego. Do not make a song and dance or you will be seen
as a fool.

Monday 12th

You begin to wonder where your passion for being
unique has led you. Higher education and travel have
always interested you and set you apart from friends and
family members but now you feel that you are left alone.
Is there no-one who is on your wavelength Sagittarius?

Tuesday 13th

The Sun sits opposite retrograde Mars and laughs at the
tantrums he is having. Is this you having a meltdown
and acting like a spoilt child? Mercury goes retrograde
tomorrow so use this energy to get all your devices
backed up. Double check travel plans now.

Wednesday 14th

Mercury retrograde begins. This will be a difficult
one for you because as you know, he is excavating
your psyche right now and has already made you feel
uncomfortable. Venus and the Moon sit together making
work a happy place to be. Meditate upon this for a
moment. Find your self-worth.

Thursday 15th

There could be power struggles within your social
network today. Who is the boss? People may want to drag
you down into an abyss but this is nothing to do with you
so stay away from the edge. The Moon enters this sector
and you feel the need to mediate the situation.

113

Friday 16th

Today there is a New Moon in your social sector. You may have noticed that some friends have disappeared from your life. These may have only been online acquaintances. This Moon asks that you set intentions around the groups you belong to. Not all are worth your time.

Saturday 17th

You may be deeply wounded today. The Moon sits on Mercury and both are opposite Uranus. This means that whatever Mercury has found, maybe an old wound or something you have refused to acknowledge, will surface. Do not pick at an old scab, give it the air it needs to heal.

Sunday 18th

You have a chance to learn a hard lesson today Sagittarius. Saturn is in contact with the Sun and these tend to show where authority figures influence you. This can make you rebellious or humble. Maybe it is you that is the authority and you question your leadership.

Monday 19th

Jupiter is getting messages from both Venus and Mars today. It is likely that there will be some exaggeration of points of view now. Women will win the day as Venus has a nice connection whereas men are being put in their places. Things could get out of hand.

Tuesday 20th

You may be pulled in two different directions now. The Moon in your sign is asking you to dream up a do-able vision of your future. Thoughts of the past make you lack the confidence to go after your goals. Meanwhile, Mercury is asking that you watch what you say today.

Wednesday 21st

Venus is sweet-talking men today. Her feminine charms can come in useful in the workplace now. If there is something you want to change, the chances are that under this influence you make it happen. Do not be afraid to use gentle persuasion today.

Thursday 22nd

The Sun now moves into your dreams sector and will light up the dark areas for Mercury to find his way around. You feel more optimistic about being able to sort out your worries as the Moon passes through your money sector unimpeded by retrograde planets.

Friday 23rd

Your communications sector may see you making short trips today. All is good in the workplace and you are getting the job done with limited pressure. You may feel some anxiety as the Moon connects with retrograde Mercury. This could mean that you need to repeat a conversation you have had recently.

Saturday 24th

Today you may get more responsibility in the workplace. You have been appraised and found to be a valuable member of the team. This could be a welcome surprise and can help you out with your financial difficulties. Take it on board, you deserve it.

Sunday 25th

Mercury is nowhere to be found. His excavation of your psyche has halted and you feel this. You could be wondering what he is up to, what will be his next move. Be assured that he is doing his best to make you feel comfortable with the darkness within. He is, after all, mining for gold.

Monday 26th

There will be pleasant surprises coming your way. An easy-going family event warms your heart and you feel good with your tribe today. Chatter is easy and people around you show their appreciation of who you are as an individual within the family group. Enjoy this day.

Tuesday 27th

Family merges and pulls together now. The Moon is sitting with Neptune who can dissolve boundaries. This is not always a good thing but today it means that family connections are important and nurturing. Your urge to stand alone is put to one side and you become part of the clan.

Wednesday 28th

Today is like a bookend day where you can either feel hemmed in or supported. Venus enters your social sector while Mercury retrogrades back into it. There may be some tension with friends. Your social calendar could be full to brimming now and you may not have time for everyone.

Thursday 29th

The Moon meets a weary Mars in your creative sector. Your artistic pursuits have been paused for a while and you get the itch to start them back up again, Unfortunately, you do not have the energy right now. These will still be here for you when Mars turns direct again.

Friday 30th

Mundane activities keep you happy today. You go along with your day, do the nine to five and have room left over for your own needs. This is the type of day which satisfies you. No tension, time for everything and chores all finished. Well done.

Saturday 31st

Today there is a Blue Moon in your health and duties sector. This is a second Full Moon in a calendar month. This Moon sits on top of Uranus so expect the unexpected today and join in any Halloween parties going on. Enjoy the thrill of this fun holiday.

NOVEMBER

. . . .

Sunday 1st
With all the recent exploration in your dreams sector,
you may now be feeling the need for a spiritual
connection. You look for a teacher or a guru. Revelations
from deep within you have come up and might be earth-
shattering but you now know what to do with them.

Monday 2nd
The Moon moves into your relationship sector and
makes a helpful connection to Saturn. Talking with
a partner or an influential person will give you some
new ideas. The world is bigger than you think and
there are options available to you that may have not
been visible before now.

Tuesday 3rd
Conversations with both sexes today can help you
form an impression of how you relate to people. You
will understand how your communication style differs
whether it is a man or a woman you are talking to. What
do you learn from this? Which sex can teach you the
most?

Wednesday 4th

Mercury goes direct today. He will once more travel over the last degrees of your social sector and this too can help you see how you relate. Close friends see one side of you, online friends another. You have a knack of adopting different personas depending on who you are interacting with.

Thursday 5th

Today you may feel vulnerable. Your recent discoveries into the relating styles you use have made you feel uncertain about yourself. You would rather stay at home in your own little world. Occult or taboo subjects interest you but you are not about to open up about this just yet.

Friday 6th

The Moon is making a tense connection to Mars and you may feel drained of energy. Nothing is getting done regarding your creative pursuits or expressing yourself right now. This is frustrating you. Begrudgingly, you put these aside in favour of more pressing matters. You feel that no-one is listening.

Saturday 7th

As the Moon enters your travel sector, you wish to get yourself out there and be seen and heard. This can make you rather pushy and no-one likes a show-off. You must learn to just be yourself Sagittarius, you are perfect as you are. You are a unique individual.

Sunday 8th

You will be as stubborn as an ox now. Your opinion is the only right one and no other will do. You may argue with authority figures. You have a right to your opinion but so does everyone else. Do not voice yours unless you are prepared to hear others.

Monday 9th

A battle of the sexes will occur today. This could also be a conflict between yourself and another. The Moon is in your work sector so be careful not to upset the boss now. There is an 'us' and 'them' battle going on. Which side are you on?

Tuesday 10th

Mercury hangs around in the last degree of your social sector. He has been there twice before in recent days so take this as a warning. There is something you need to deal with regarding your associates. Put something right or apologise now before it is too late and you lose a friend.

Wednesday 11th

Once again the winged messenger heads for your dreams sector. This area deals with your solitude and how you manage that. You may have had enough of this lately and resort to mind-numbing substances such as drugs or alcohol. Try chocolate and trash TV instead.

Thursday 12th

There are lovely connections happening in the sky today, make the most of them. You feel an emotional pull toward friendship groups. Venus adds her charm and restores harmony. Any kind of transformation you would like to make is favoured now by a Jupiter and Pluto meet-up in your finance sector.

Friday 13th

Your emotions are intense now. You may begin to see the benefit of Mercury's digging around. The Moon enters your dreams sector and once more you may want to self-soothe with substances. If you choose to do this, the Jupiter and Pluto meet-up can make this get out of control.

Saturday 14th

Today you may feel extremely tired. Mars is turning around and will go direct again. Although this is good news, you may feel this like a stone attached to your ankles. Get through the day and you will see the change in your energy. Things you are passionate about will be re-started.

Sunday 15th

A New Moon in your dreams sector gives you the chance to firmly make resolutions regarding your shadow side. Mercury has given you the lead and now you must make it into gold. There may be a struggle with women today. Do not try to control others now.

Monday 16th

Venus calls the shots today and dances around your social sector trying to get her own way. You or someone around you could be acting like a stroppy child. An elder will come along and cut you, or the stroppy child down to size. Stop being a drama queen.

Tuesday 17th

Do be careful with your words today. Mercury is sitting opposite Uranus and this placement usually means that words spoken can be hurtful. This may also mean that you have a fantastic idea that has come from nowhere. If you have an 'aha' moment today, use it wisely.

Wednesday 18th

Actions and emotions are at odds today. Emotionally, you are consumed with thoughts about finances and what you own. However, your actions speak otherwise and you could be making a spontaneous purchase. Use your restless energy to make something. Be proud that your enthusiasm is back but do not abuse it.

Thursday 19th

The Moon passes over your money sector. Things do not look as bad as they have done all year. You have learned more about taking responsibility for yourself and your spending. A more mature you has emerged which makes you proud. Do not undo all the hard work Sagittarius.

Friday 20th

Your communications sector gets a hit today and you will find that you just cannot say right for saying wrong. You put your foot in your mouth with most of your conversations and can come off looking like an idiot. Do not worry, this will not last long and people will forget.

Saturday 21st

At last, the Sun moves into your sign. You will feel the heat now. You are chomping at the bit and have your Archer's bow and arrow ready to fire at your goals. Venus has moved into your last sector of dreams, solitude and secrets.

Sunday 22nd

Is it family time? Spend the day with your loved ones and share your enthusiasm. Today you will light up any family gathering from the minute they see you skipping down the path. This feels like the preparation for a race. The air is filled with anticipation around you. Let your arrow loose.

Monday 23rd

Your mood is still light-hearted and adventurous. You have a goal in mind now. This is you at your best. Dreams seem more attainable. The worries that have followed you all year have dissolved. At least for now. Start the race while you can see the road ahead.

Tuesday 24th

Mercury is still in your psyche and today is telling Neptune what he has found. You already know what this is and this is why you are skipping. Enthusiasm fills you and you return to your creative projects. This influence may also mean that you have fallen in love.

Wednesday 25th

Mars is direct and still in his own sign. He has picked up speed since he turned and this is where your extra energy is coming from. You feel fired up and raring to go. Mercury's lead is already being turned into gold in the fire of your heart.

Thursday 26th

The Moon meets with Mars today. This could be a very sexy day for you. Mars is happy and driven, the Moon is emotional and wants to connect. Mars also rules your sex drive. One warning though, do not be frivolous and overspend. This is not something you want to be doing again.

Friday 27th

Venus in your dreams sector is quite the siren here. She may bewitch you easily. Please be sure that what you are looking at is the real thing and not a trick. There are other planetary connections which can rock you out of your happy boat now.

Saturday 28th

It is the weekend but you may need to come back down to earth for a while. You must remember that life goes on while you are on cloud nine. There are duties that you must attend to now. This needs to be a busy Saturday of chores.

Sunday 29th

Anything you feel rising from your subconscious will be felt in a big way today. Mercury is telling Jupiter what he has found and Jupiter tells the whole world. You might feel vulnerable and exposed. Take this lightly Sagittarius, laugh at yourself. Both Mercury and Jupiter like laughter.

Monday 30th

Today there is a Full Moon in your relationship sector. What have you been working towards for the last six months regarding partners? Under this illumination, you will be able to spot if anything new is going to last. It may be an illusion you have grasped onto with rose-tinted spectacles.

DECEMBER

. . . .

Tuesday 1st
Mercury now moves into your sign. This heralds a busy time of communication and connecting. You will be researching all those places on your bucket list. New connections will be made with people who can help you go where you want to go. Your curiosity is alive and kicking now.

Wednesday 2nd
The Moon moves into your sex, death and rebirth sector. Unlike previous months when the Moon was here, you are now keen to explore secret and taboo subjects. You may be getting to know someone new on an intensely deep level. This is someone you can be vulnerable with.

Thursday 3rd
Whilst you are probing the depths of a new intimate relationship, you must ensure that you are not pushy and forceful. You can come across as being too demanding now. Be mindful of people's boundaries. Deepening connections must come from both parties. Mutual respect is always necessary.

Friday 4th

Today you may be thrilling someone with tales of your adventures and travel. You tell a good story but you must remember not to show-off. There is a chance that your enthusiasm and experience can overwhelm the listener. In which case, you will be seen as a know it all.

Saturday 5th

Your energy is back on track with your emotional life and a balance is found. However, the Moon is making a poor connection to Uranus in your health and duties sector. This means that you could be irritated that mundane activities take away some of your weekend time.

Sunday 6th

Dreamy, floaty energy comes from Venus in your hidden sector making a smooth connection to Neptune in your family sector. Venus mixes up a potion that makes this day surreal. You may be doing this to yourself with drugs, alcohol or sex. Whatever your poison, play nicely and be careful.

Monday 7th

Monday comes and you settle back down into the working week. There could be a nice surprise waiting for you at work. You have great ideas and plans at this time. There is a chance that you find a solution to something that has been niggling you at work. Genius thinking is the energy of the day.

Tuesday 8th

Saturn is sitting in the very last degree of your money
sector. This point is important and is a warning to
consider all that you have learned here before he
moves on. You will have ten days to complete anything
outstanding regarding finances, resources and the legacy
you leave behind.

Wednesday 9th

The Moon moves into your social sector. A midweek
evening with friends is possible. You could also be
enjoying your friendship groups online. Chatty Mercury
is joining the party and this is a great chance to connect
with new people who share your interests. Don't stay up
all night Sagittarius.

Thursday 10th

Females may charm you now. Watch out for women who
appear witch-like as they will put a spell on you and make
you do their bidding. The Sun in your sign is connecting
to Neptune and you could be fooled or the opposite, you
could see false people for who they really are.

Friday 11th

The Sun joins a point in the sky where the past is
brought back to your mind. Meanwhile, the Moon
slips into your hidden sector of dreams. You will be
reminiscing about someone or something from a long
time ago. A deeply melancholic state comes over you.
Regrets fill you.

Saturday 12th

The Moon is now sitting with Venus. Think of this like a Priestess and Sorceress discussing their art. Women will feature highly now. Mothers and other maternal figures, partners and lovers will all be floating around in your head. How have women in your life influenced you?

Sunday 13th

The Moon comes up from the underworld of your psyche and into the sector which deals with 'self'. This is a more accessible area and where you can deal with emotions easily. You can brush them off as they are more superficial now. Energy from the Sun in your sign is optimistic.

Monday 14th

There is an important New Moon today. This one sits on the point of looking to the past. It also joins Mercury who is contemplating life gone by too. You know that it is necessary to change something and make good intentions now. This is the perfect opportunity.

Tuesday 15th

Venus enters your sign now. She will bring her gifts of
beauty, harmony, love and money. She also deals with
self-worth. Here, she will end the year by making you take
a hard look at how you handle money and responsibility.
This is tied up with your self-worth.

Wednesday 16th

Saturn finally moves into your communications sector.
You will be learning about how you can connect to
the wider world. Friends far and wide will come under
scrutiny for the next two and a half years. Some friends
will be dropped. You may be antagonistic and raise a
revolution now.

Thursday 17th

The Moon drifts by the planets that have been causing
you trouble this year. She met Pluto yesterday and will
fly by Jupiter and Saturn today. You give thanks for the
hard lessons they have given you. This can make you feel
proud and at the same time, very humble.

Friday 18th

Mercury is silent now. He is sitting in the light of the
midwinter sun and receiving new information for the
year ahead. A time of silent contemplation will be highly
beneficial to you now. Go inside yourself, meditate and
listen to your inner voice of calm.

Saturday 19th

Jupiter bids farewell to your money sector. Normally he would have expanded your finances but this year, combined with the other planets, he has expanded your debt. Nevertheless, you have managed to sort this out now. Do not overspend over the festive season and undo all your hard work.

Sunday 20th

A joyful union takes place in the heavens today. Jupiter and Saturn meet at the exact same degree in your communications sector. You will feel this as a push-pull energy but you must learn to ride it. Breathe in, breathe out. Speak, listen. Be active, be passive. This will help you to be an excellent communicator.

Monday 21st

The longest night, the Winter Solstice is here. The Sun is now in your money sector, this is good news. Mercury joins the Sun as his messenger. He is also the planet of merchants so you may want to consider buying and selling while he is in this sector.

Tuesday 22nd

After the stillness of the last few days, you ache for some action. Your creative sector is getting some Moon energy and you are drawn back to projects you are passionate about. You may show your divine essence now in all its glory. Make art to be proud of.

Wednesday 23rd

Your energy levels are revving up for the holidays.
There may be some control issue, however. This influence
may also mean that you need to watch your health as you
are likely to overdo all the good things now. There may be
some arguments between men and women.

Thursday 24th

The Moon dips into your health and duties sector. There
is much work to do. If you are the one who is organising
the activities for the holiday season then your mind will
be focused on that. Alternatively, you could be the one
being waited on and eating or drinking too much.

Friday 25th

Happy Christmas Sagittarius! The energy today is full
of surprises - well, it is Christmas! Fathers and sons
can feature now as Jupiter and Saturn are still on the
same degree. Conversations flow easily and it looks like
Christmas will go well for you. Enjoy your day.

Saturday 26th

There is still nice, easy energy for the festive season.
Family dreams and visions are mutual now. Everyone is
happy and floats around in a Neptune sea of belonging
and merging. There are jobs to be done today but these
are shared and no-one feels over-worked.

Sunday 27th

The Moon moves into your relationship sector and you will concentrate more on your partner today. The two of you can chat until the sun goes down. Conversations can go from the sublime to the ridiculous. There can be a lot of laughter to be had if you let it.

Monday 28th

Today you may approach your partner with a vision of a brave new world. Do not be surprised if they do not buy it straight away. This is something that has been inside of you for a long time and they will need persuading that this can work for them too.

Tuesday 29th

The last Full Moon of the year falls in your sector of sex, death and rebirth. You may feel despondent now if you have not had the courage to open up to someone close. If you were brave, then this Moon will highlight the good things that have come from that.

Wednesday 30th

The Moon opposite Mercury gives you the chance to review and assess how you deal with authority figures. Maternal and paternal figures who have formed your identity will enter your thoughts, you may even be considering your own nurturing and leadership roles. Today you must self-soothe and have a day free from family.

Thursday 31st

Today the energy suggests that there may be some issues that you cannot control. You must go with the flow now Sagittarius. A New Year's Eve at home with good food and company may be just the right recipe for a happy end to the year. Look back and give thanks.

Sagittarius

. . . .

PEOPLE WHO
SHARE YOUR SIGN

PEOPLE WHO
SHARE YOUR SIGN

·················

The free spirits of the zodiac can be easy to identify
with their expansive thinking and lively approach to
life. From Winston Churchill to Nicki Minaj, it feels
like these inspiring Sagittarians where placed on
Earth to motivate the masses. Whether this dual sign
is influenced more by their intellectual mind or their
physical strength, Sagittarians' daring attitudes will
see them go far. Discover which of these optimistic
Sagittarians share your exact birthday and see if you
can spot the similarities.

November 23rd

Alexis Ren (1996), Miley Cyrus (1992), Snooki (1987), Kelly Brook (1979), Zoë Ball (1970), Vincent Cassel (1966), Nicolás Maduro, 63rd President of Venezuela (1962), John Schnatter (1961), Ludovico Einaudi (1955)

November 24th

Sarah Hyland (1990), Katherine Heigl (1978), Colin Hanks (1977), Stephen Merchant (1974), Shirley Henderson (1965), Billy Connolly (1942), Dale Carnegie (1888), Henri de Toulouse-Lautrec (1864)

November 25th

Katie Cassidy (1986), Gaspard Ulliel (1984), Joel Kinnaman (1979), Christina Applegate (1971), John F. Kennedy Jr. (1960), Ben Stein (1944), Ricardo Montalbán (1920), Karl Benz (1844)

November 26th

Rita Ora (1990), Danny Welbeck (1990), Tamsin Egerton (1988), Chris Hughes (1983), DJ Khaled (1975), Peter Facinelli (1973), Tina Turner (1939), Charles M. Schulz (1922)

November 27th

Professor Green (1983), Robin Givens (1964), Yulia
Tymoshenko, Former Prime Minister of Ukraine (1960),
William Fichtner (1956), Jil Sander (1943), Manolo Blahnik
(1942), Jimi Hendrix (1942), Bruce Lee (1940)

November 28th

Karen Gillan (1987), Trey Songz (1984), Mary Elizabeth
Winstead (1984), Daniel Henney (1979), Jon Stewart (1962),
Martin Clunes (1961), Alfonso Cuarón (1961), Judd Nelson
(1959), Ed Harris (1950), Friedrich Engels (1820)

November 29th

Diego Boneta (1990), Lauren German (1978), Chadwick
Boseman (1977), Anna Faris (1976), Ryan Giggs (1973),
Don Cheadle (1964), Jacques Chirac, Former President of
France (1932), Jackie Stallone (1921), C. S. Lewis (1898)

November 30th

Kaley Cuoco (1985), Chrissy Teigen (1985), Elisha
Cuthbert (1982), Steve Aoki (1977), Ben Stiller (1965),
Gary Lineker (1960), Billy Idol (1955), Ridley Scott (1937),
Winston Churchill (1874), Lucy Maud Montgomery (1874),
Mark Twain (1835)

December 1st

Chanel Iman (1990), Zoë Kravitz (1988), Vance Joy (1987),
Janelle Monáe (1985), Sarah Silverman (1970), Pablo
Escobar (1949), Bette Midler (1945), Woody Allen (1935)

December 2nd

Charlie Puth (1991), Alfred Enoch (1988), Teairra Marí (1987),
Action Bronson (1983), Aaron Rodgers (1983), Britney
Spears (1981), Nelly Furtado (1978), Lucy Liu (1968)

December 3rd

Amanda Seyfried (1985), Dascha Polanco (1982), Jenna
Dewan (1980), Holly Marie Combs (1973), Brendan Fraser
(1968), Daryl Hannah (1960), Julianne Moore (1960), Ozzy
Osbourne (1948)

December 4th
Niykee Heaton (1994), Tyra Banks (1973), Kevin Sussman (1970), JAY Z (1969), Fred Armisen (1966), Marisa Tomei (1964), Jeff Bridges (1949), Albert Bandura (1925)

December 5th
Anthony Martial (1995), Frankie Muniz (1985), Ronnie O'Sullivan (1975), Paula Patton (1975), Eddie the Eagle (1963), Bhumibol Adulyadej, 9th King of Thailand (1927), Walt Disney (1901), Werner Heisenberg (1901)

December 6th
Stefanie Scott (1996), Alberto Contador (1982), Noel Clarke (1975), Sarah Rafferty (1972), Judd Apatow (1967), Nick Park (1958), Peter Buck (1956), Agnes Moorehead (1900)

December 7th
Nicholas Hoult (1989), Emily Browning (1988), Aaron Carter (1987), Dan Bilzerian (1980), John Terry (1980), Sara Bareilles (1979), Jennifer Carpenter (1979), Noam Chomsky (1928)

December 8th

AnnaSophia Robb (1993), Amir Khan (1986), Nicki Minaj (1982), Ian Somerhalder (1978), Dominic Monaghan (1976), Sinéad O'Connor (1966), Teri Hatcher (1964), Kim Basinger (1953), John Banville (1945)

December 9th

Simon Helberg (1980), Jesse Metcalfe (1978), Kurt Angle (1968), Felicity Huffman (1962), Donny Osmond (1957), John Malkovich (1953), Dame Judi Dench (1934), Kirk Douglas (1916)

December 10th

Teyana Taylor (1990), Gonzalo Higuaín (1987), Kim Sears (1987), Raven Symone (1985), Emmanuelle Chriqui (1975), Susanna Reid (1970), Kenneth Branagh (1960), Michael Clarke Duncan (1957-2012), Emily Dickinson (1830-1886)

December 11th

Hailee Steinfeld (1996), Mos Def (1973), Mo'Nique (1967), DJ Yella (1967), Marco Pierre White (1961), Nikki Sixx (1958), Jermaine Jackson (1954), Pranab Mukherjee, 13th President of India (1935)

December 12th
Yuvraj Singh (1981), Mayim Bialik (1975), Mädchen Amick (1970), Jennifer Connelly (1970), Regina Hall (1970), Sheila E. (1957), Bill Nighy (1949), Frank Sinatra (1915), Edvard Munch (1863)

December 13th
Katherine Schwarzenegger (1989), Taylor Swift (1989), Amy Lee (1981), Tom DeLonge (1975), Jamie Foxx (1967), Steve Buscemi (1957), Christopher Plummer (1929), Dick Van Dyke (1925)

December 14th
Tori Kelly (1992), Vanessa Hudgens (1988), Michael Owen (1979), Miranda Hart (1972), Natascha McElhone (1969), Dilma Rousseff, 36th President of Brazil (1947), Jane Birkin (1946), Stan Smith (1946), B. K. S. Iyengar (1918), George VI, Former King of the United Kingdom (1895)

December 15th

Jesse Lingard (1992), Keylor Navas (1986), Camilla Luddington (1983), Charlie Cox (1982), Michelle Dockery (1981), Adam Brody (1979), Don Johnson (1949), Tim Conway (1933), Gustave Eiffel (1832)

December 16th

Zara Larsson (1997), Anna Popplewell (1988), Theo James (1984), Danielle Lloyd (1983), Krysten Ritter (1981), Miranda Otto (1967), Benjamin Bratt (1963), Philip K. Dick (1928), Wassily Kandinsky (1866)

December 17th

Dynamo (1982), Katheryn Winnick (1977), Milla Jovovich (1975), Sarah Paulson (1974), Giovanni Ribisi (1974), Rian Johnson (1973), Eugene Levy (1946), Muhammadu Buhari, President of Nigeria (1942), Pope Francis (1936)

December 18th

Ashley Benson (1989), Christina Aguilera (1980), Katie Holmes (1978), Sia Furler (1975), DMX (1970), Brad Pitt (1963), Jonathan Cainer (1957), Ray Liotta (1954), Steven Spielberg (1946), Keith Richards (1943), Joseph Stalin (1878), J. J. Thomson (1856)

December 19th

Alexis Sánchez (1988), Karim Benzema (1987), Jake Gyllenhaal (1980), Alyssa Milano (1972), Tyson Beckford (1970), Richard Hammond (1969), Jennifer Beals (1963), Til Schweiger (1963), Maurice White (1941), Édith Piaf (1915)

December 20th

JoJo (1990), Bugzy Malone (1990), Bob Morley (1984), Jonah Hill (1983), Lara Stone (1983), Ashley Cole (1980), Chris Robinson (1966), Jenny Agutter (1952), Uri Geller (1946), Peter Criss (1945)

December 21st

Steven Yeun (1983), Tom Payne (1982), Emmanuel Macron, President of France (1977), Kiefer Sutherland (1966), Ray Romano (1957), Jane Kaczmarek (1955), Chris Evert (1954), Samuel L. Jackson (1948), Jane Fonda (1937), Phil Donahue (1935)

'Workmen and Workwomen' by Philip Homan Miller (1874) at Salford City Art Gallery. The painting shows a family of Cheshire salt makers, including a mother breast-feeding her baby.

The Salt Industry

Andrew and Annelise Fielding

A Shire book

Published in 2006 by Shire Publications Ltd,
Cromwell House, Church Street, Princes Risborough,
Buckinghamshire HP27 9AA, UK.
(Website: www.shirebooks.co.uk)

British Library Cataloguing in Publication Data:
Fielding, Andrew.
The salt industry. – (Shire album; 454)
1. Salt industry and trade – Great Britain – History I. Title
II. Fielding, Annelise 338.4'76223632'0941
ISBN-10: 0 7478 0648 9.

Front cover illustrations (clockwise from top left): *Hollow pyramidal hopper crystals manufactured by the Maldon Crystal Salt Company. Four salt workers raking, skimming, tubbing and happing salt; 'happing' was squaring up and smoothing down the lumps. Modern reproductions of salt pigs and other containers for table salt. The last lumpman at the Lion Salt Works, Northwich, using a skimmer to fill salt tubs.*

ACKNOWLEDGEMENTS
The authors would like to thank particularly Vale Royal Borough Council; the Trustees and volunteers of the Lion Salt Works Trust; George Twigg; Paul Barford; James Fawn, Colchester Archaeology Group; Paul Gilman, Essex County Council; David Cranstone, Cranstone Consulting; Simon Hayhow, Fleetwood Museum, Lancashire County Council; Allan Hughes; Tom Lane.
    Photographs and other illustrations are acknowledged as follows: Caroline Breen, Maldon Crystal Salt Company, page 20 (centre); from Calvert, *Salt in Cheshire* (1915), front cover (top right), pages 7 (bottom), 11 (both), 26 (top), 29, 30 (both), 31 (top), 35, 38 (top), 43, 44 (top, lower centre and bottom); Cheshire County Council, pages 7 (top), 42; Poul Christensen, Læsø Salt Works, Denmark, page 27; Andrew Fielding, pages 4, 23 (top), 39 (all), 40 (top), 45 (bottom); Annelise Fielding, pages 14 (top), 16 (both), 17 (top), 25 (top), 36, 41 (top), 44 (upper centre), 46 (top), 48 (all), 53; Rosemary Hogarth, page 28 (both); Derek Hurst, County Archaeological Service, Worcestershire County Council, pages 22 (top right), 25 (bottom); Keith Jarvis, Poole Borough Council, page 15; Rob Jones, British Salt, pages 41 (bottom), 47 (bottom); Mrs Rosemary Joy, Eday, Orkney, page 20 (top); Cadbury Lamb, page 18 (top and centre); Mikel Lander, Álava Council, Spain, page 53; Tom Lane, Heritage Trust of Lincolnshire, page 14 (bottom); David Lea-Wilson, Anglesey Sea Salt Company, page 20 (bottom); Lion Salt Works Trust, front cover (top left, bottom left, bottom right), pages 3, 5, 6, 8, 9 (top), 10 (both), 12 (all), 13, 21, 22 (bottom), 26 (bottom), 31 (centre and bottom two), 32 (all), 33 (all), 34 (all), 38 (bottom), 40 (centre), 45 (top), 46 (bottom), 47 (top and centre); Steve Liscoe, Archaeological Unit, Fife Council, page 19 (bottom); John Luzader, Living Museums of the West, Colorado, USA, page 9 (bottom); Steven Marshall, St Barbe Museum, Lymington, Hampshire, page 18 (bottom); Robina McNeil, University of Manchester Archaeology Unit, page 23 (centre and bottom); Mike Nevell, University of Manchester Archaeology Unit, page 22 (top left); Royal Commission on the Ancient and Historical Monuments of Wales, Aberystwyth, Crown copyright, page 19 (top); Salford City Art Gallery, page 1; Alan Sheen, Salt Union, page 40 (bottom); Southwold Museum, page 17 (bottom); George Twigg, page 24.

Printed in Malta by Gutenberg Press Limited, Gudja Road, Tarxien PLA 19, Malta.

Contents

Road sign, Northwich, Cheshire, warning traffic of poor visibility in the vicinity of salt works. Steam would drift around pan houses, where brine was evaporated to make white salt. The steam vapour could be as dense as fog and as road traffic increased signs were placed on roads adjacent to salt works to warn approaching drivers.

Seawater varies in its salinity around the coast but is generally 2.5 per cent.

Introduction

The production of salt by the evaporation of brine is common around the world. Salt, or sodium chloride (NaCl), occurs naturally either in solution as brine or in solid form as rock salt (halite). There are two sources of brine for white salt production in the United Kingdom. They are seawater and the brine that occurs in association with rock salt formations.

In the past salt was so important that it was taxed and controlled by governments; the taxation was not repealed in Britain until 1825. Lack of salt would cause great hardship because it was essential for the preservation of meat, fish, butter and cheese and also for the making of other staples such as bread, where salt controls the action of the yeast. Salt was used for glazing ceramics, from bellarmines, jam jars and drain pipes to Doulton vases, and salt glazes are still used today by artist potters. Such was the status of salt that special containers were made to show it off at the table, the wealthy using silver and gold table salts. Ordinary people used containers made of ceramic or wood. Salt boxes and salt pigs kept salt dry in the kitchen; they are important examples of folk art and display regional styles.

The antiquarian W. M. Hardy, in his book *Old Swanage and Purbeck Past and Present*, discusses the effect of the salt tax in the early nineteenth century and says that people living in Corfe Castle, Dorset, who could not walk to the coast at Swanage and back (a round trip of 10 miles or 16 km) would ask the flour carters to bring with them a bucket of seawater to mix with the flour in lieu of salt in order to make bread. He also reports that when a poor man killed a pig he would have to sell half

The hooded salt pig, kit or dolly (back right) prevented salt from becoming damp. Open dishes, such as capstan salts (blue and white examples at front) or Wakefield pillar salts (front right), were used as table salts. Bottles, such as the 'bellarmines', were salt-glazed. A sixteenth-century 'salt lady' (left) in the National Museum of Wales, Cardiff, was a table piece designating whether one was 'above' or 'below the salt'. The modern salt pig (back) is by Jean Knowles. All other pieces are reproductions by John Hudson.

of it to buy the salt to preserve the remaining half. Although we are today concerned with reducing our salt intake, such anecdotes remind us that as recently as the early twentieth century salt was not regarded in the same light. Before the use of refrigeration and the development of modern food-processing industries salt was an essential part of our lives.

Only one per cent of salt production is sold as table or cooking salt today; the rest goes to food manufacturing and the chemical industries. Salt is used extensively in dairy products and other food processing, in tanning, for water softening, for clearing snow and ice from the roads, as a fertiliser, and in the chemical industry as a raw material in the manufacture of chlorine, caustic soda and soda ash, which in turn are used by many other industries. The United Kingdom salt industry is currently the ninth largest in the world.

Salt is a bulky commodity, difficult to transport, but it has been produced industrially from the earliest times. Even today the economics of salt making are linked to issues involving consumers, transport, labour and fuel. This book looks at how salt has been made, where it was made and how the scale of production has changed through time to provide a commodity that is now in everyone's kitchen and in many other products, used on a daily basis and taken very much for granted.

Brine and rock salt

Around the coast brine can be taken directly from the sea as seawater. The alternative source of brine is from natural brine springs inland. These occur where rock salt (halite) is close to the surface. Rainwater percolates through the ground and dissolves the rock salt, forming brine streams. These formerly came to the surface as brine springs in the river valleys but the water table has been lowered and they no longer do so.

Natural brine can be pumped from the underground brine streams, known in Cheshire as 'wild brine'. It can also be sourced as 'artificial brine' created by 'solution mining' rock salt by pumping fresh water into the rock to form a cavity, forcing brine back to the surface. This process is also known as 'controlled brine pumping'.

Brine occurs in different strengths, depending on how much salt the water is holding. To make the strongest brine possible, weak brine can be strengthened by dissolving into it mined rock salt or manufactured white salt crystals.

Natural brine streams can be eight times saltier than seawater, almost a saturated brine solution in which the groundwater can hold no more

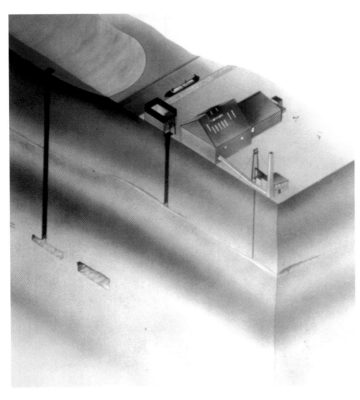

Cross-section below the Lion Salt Works near Northwich, Cheshire, showing two levels of rock salt strata. The stratum nearest the surface is the wet rock head, along which the brine streams run. The narrow boreholes through which the Lion Salt Works pumped brine run down to this level. The lower stratum is the dry bed. The Adelaide Mine took rock salt from this level. It collapsed in 1928 because water got in and eroded the rock salt pillars, which supported the roof of the mine. The pit ponies had to be destroyed, being too big to return to the surface. The water in the flash is fresh, draining rainwater from the surrounding fields.

In solution mining water is pumped into rock salt to dissolve it and create cavities from which brine can be made. Through the careful input of air at the surface, cavities are developed and controlled to prevent them rising upwards, merging together or collapsing. Special cavities can be created in the rock salt strata that allow storage below ground of gas for energy supplies.

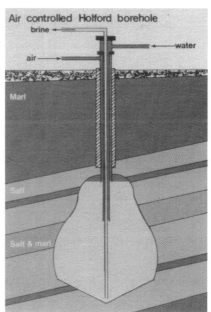

salt in solution. This greatly reduces the amount of heat required to evaporate the water and allow the salt to crystallise out of the brine solution.

Rock salt is derived from dried-up seas of the Triassic and Permian periods (about 250 million years ago). It was laid down at a time when the British Isles were much closer to the equator and were experiencing a climate of extreme heat with desert conditions. The seas evaporated, leaving behind salt crystals mixed with sand and marl blown in from the surrounding land. It is these sands and marls which give Cheshire rock salt its characteristic pink-orange appearance and which provide the 'grit' for spreading on roads in the winter.

Cross-section across the Northwich salt fields published in Calvert's book 'Salt in Cheshire' (1915). It shows the extent of the layering and faulting of the Cheshire rock salt strata between Northwich and Winsford.

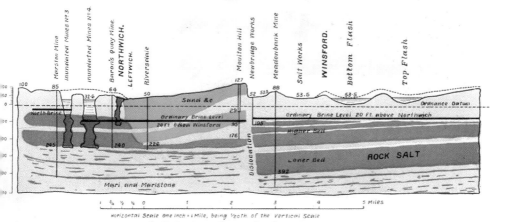

Salt-making processes

British people on holiday overseas (in places such as the Guerande, France; Figuera da Foz, Portugal; Torrevieja, Spain; Piran, Slovenia; Pomorie, Bulgaria; Lesvos, Greece; and Gozo, Malta) may have seen salinas, in which brine (seawater) is evaporated by the heat of the sun to make white salt. This is not possible in the British climate and nowadays most salt in the United Kingdom is made by vacuum evaporation. Before this method was adopted, all salt made in Britain, whether from inland brine springs where groundwater has dissolved rock salt deposits, or from seawater around the coast, was made by the 'open-pan' evaporation process. The material from which the pans were made has changed over the centuries from ceramic to lead and then to iron, which continued in use until pans made of modern, corrosion-resistant materials took over in the twentieth century.

White salt is made by the evaporation of brine until pure crystals of sodium chloride are precipitated from the solution. These crystals grow larger until they sink to the bottom of the evaporating container. Eventually, when sufficient crystals have formed, they are drawn to the side of the container and lifted out of the solution. At this point they are generally allowed to drain before either being put into containers for drainage and drying or piled in heaps and sold loose in bulk.

In Britain the first stage in the production of sea salt was *solar evaporation*, to concentrate seawater brine in lagoons before the evaporation could be completed using artificial heat.

Seawater brine was also obtained by washing shore sand. *Sleeching* was a process by which salt-impregnated sand was collected, air-dried and put into a pit called a kinch, in which sea or fresh water was poured over the sand until eventually brine filtered out into a cistern. This process was

Three lead salt pans, believed to be early medieval, were found at Bostock, Cheshire, near the River Dane. They are now in the care of the Lion Salt Works Trust. Although nested together when found, two are marked with raised crosses and the third has raised dots on the reverse. Over twenty lead salt pans have now been found in Cheshire. Only three have been found in the rest of north-west Europe.

Salt in ceramic containers, showing the effects of a porous fabric (left) and a harder-fired, non-porous fabric (right). Liquor soaking through the body wall of the low-fired containers demonstrates the effect of salt crystallising out on the outer surface. Non-porous fabrics hinder the drying of crystals. Some ceramic containers were used as storage vessels in which the salt crystals were drained, dried and carried. In this process bitter salts might drain through the walls of the porous containers. Briquetage containers are also found away from the production sites, distributed by the trade in salt.

repeated until the brine would float an egg. Eventually the kinch would be emptied, creating huge sleeching mounds of waste material. It was a medieval technique used particularly in the Solway Firth and also in Lincolnshire, where it was known as *muldefang*.

In the *pot process* brine is placed in ceramic or metal pots, or similar containers, in which the salt crystallises during evaporation over a fire. In Scotland and north-east England a variation of the pot process was used in which seawater was boiled without any previous concentration.

In the *open pan process* the brine is evaporated in a wide flat-based pan supported over a fire or flue. The temperature and speed of evaporation

This reconstruction of the pot process, evaporating seawater at Seaside, Oregon, USA, in 2003, celebrated the bicentenary of the Lewis and Clark expedition, the first crossing of the continent. They took with them salt makers, who were needed to make salt on the Pacific coast to preserve food for their return journey to St Louis. Two tin-lined copper kettles were used for evaporating seawater. Copper kettles not lined with tin produce green salt polluted with copper sulphate and copper chloride. Evaporating brine within ceramic pots is the origin of the pot process. If the pot boils dry, the salt will cake on the inside and will contain bitter salts. If, however, the pot is continually topped up with brine, the salt will eventually crystallise out of the saturated solution and can be scooped out, leaving the bitter salts behind in the solution liquor. This is poured away and the process starts again.

This is a sophisticated way of making salt devised by salt makers who understood the problems of making open pan salt in ceramic vessels using seawater. By adding cool, weak brine to the furthest pan from the fire (on the left of the photograph) and transferring it from pan to pan towards the hot end of the oven, the brine is concentrated and salt is crystallised. This method is economical with fuel and reduces any risk of thermal shock breaking the fragile clay pans.

are varied to produce crystals that are fine, medium or coarse – the quicker the evaporation, the finer the crystals. The brine is replenished as the crystals are drawn out to prevent crystals of bitter salts adhering to the sodium chloride. Periodically the fires are put out and the liquor is drained away. At the Lion Salt Works, Cheshire, this happened once a week but in smaller pans it would have to be done more often – every three days according to some documents. At Lymington in Hampshire the brine liquor was processed further to produce Epsom salts. Though the process altered little over the centuries, metal containers replaced

Open pans became bigger as iron pans were adopted. The working platform beside the pan is called 'the hurdles'. Excavations in Nantwich show that there were wattle platforms, or hurdles, beside medieval salt pans. Using saturated brine, it took half a ton of coal to make one ton of salt in an open pan. As fuel costs rose, manufacturers experimented to try to save fuel and eventually vacuum evaporation was adopted.

An early photograph of a vacuum evaporating vessel constructed at Winsford in 1905. This can be compared to the modern vacuum evaporators used today by British Salt at Middlewich (see page 41).

Different grades of salt were produced for different customers. This illustration was published by Calvert in his book 'Salt in Cheshire' (1915). The samples illustrated were produced by the Hodgkinson Process at the same time and in one operation: 1, finest table salt, without grinding; 2, dairy or butter salt; 3, common salt; 4, coarse common salt for curing, etc; 5, no.1 fishery salt; 6, no. 2 fishery salt. Thomas Ward travelled the world collecting salt samples, which he donated to the first salt museum, established in the John Brunner Library in 1889. Modern salt manufacturers stress the purity of salt and its cheapness, whereas sea salt producers in particular emphasise the natural mineral content and the special nature of the crystal shape.

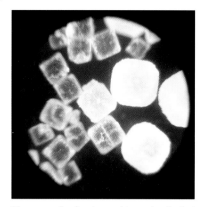

Vacuum salt showing cubic and spherical crystals made from purified brine (magnification x 4).

Hollow pyramidal hopper crystals manufactured by the Maldon Crystal Salt Company (magnification x 4).

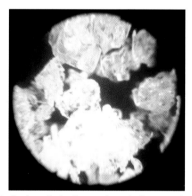

Hard, irregular, French sea salt crystals (magnification x 4).

Spiky, branched salt crystals made from unrefined brine in an open pan (magnification x 4).

ceramic ones and the fuel used changed from wood or peat to coal.

Salt refining or the *salt-on-salt process* reprocesses impure salt by re-dissolving it in weak brine to make strong brine. From the sixteenth century some sites in Essex reprocessed impure sea salt carried down the coast from the north or imported from France or the Cape Verde Islands. It was the discovery of rock salt that led to the specific development of salt refineries, often sited on the coast, where coal was used to evaporate strong brine made from the dissolution of rock salt in seawater.

Rock salt mining began in Britain after coal prospectors discovered rock salt strata in 1670 on the Marbury estate in Cheshire. Initially used for strengthening brine, rock salt nowadays has a major use for de-icing roads in winter.

Vacuum evaporation started at the beginning of the twentieth century. In this process steam is injected into sealed chambers under reduced atmospheric pressure and heats the brine. Using computer monitoring, the process is very efficient in energy and labour and produces salt very cheaply.

Sea salt making

Prehistoric coastal salt-making sites are difficult to locate. One indicator of many early sites is the pottery called briquetage, which is found in large quantities at sites around the east and south coasts of England. Along the Essex coast large residues of briquetage used in the construction of hearths, salt pans and containers during the later Iron Age have created field monuments called 'Red Hills'. Many of these sites continued into the Roman period. Many early sites have been destroyed by coastal erosion and by development, while others now lie inland, stranded as the coastline retreated and sometimes subsequently buried beneath alluvium.

Charters for south coast salterns appear in the Anglo-Saxon period from the eighth to the tenth century and in the eleventh century the Domesday Book recorded over 1195 salinas, mostly in Sussex, Kent, Norfolk and Lincolnshire. There are twelfth-century texts referring to salterns in County Durham and Cumbria but there are fewer surviving sites there.

Areas and specific sites where salt making from seawater has taken place.

An inlet on the saltmarsh at St Osyth, Essex.

Iron Age salt making on the Lincolnshire Fens. The inlets were flooded at high tide, seawater being trapped by dams as the tide receded before being transferred into tanks. Here, sand and silt settled out and some initial concentration of brine would take place before it was poured into pans and evaporated. The salt pans and their hearths were made from local clay. The peat fuel would have been cut and stacked in advance. Salt making was probably a summer activity.

A replica Romano-British farm at Upton Country Park, Poole, Dorset, based on an excavated farmstead where evidence for salt making was found on the edge of Poole Harbour.

From the eleventh century salt began to be imported in larger quantities for salting fish. West coast ports imported 'bay' salt from France, Spain and Portugal while east coast ports obtained salt from other parts of mainland Europe, especially from Luneberg in Germany.

In the thirteenth and fourteenth centuries salt was imported from western France, with wine from Bordeaux, and from Spain. By the middle of the fourteenth century the Bay of Bourgneuf in southern Brittany had a virtual monopoly of the salt trade with northern Europe. In the post-medieval period the Cape Verde Islands became an important source, shipping bay salt to England and Newfoundland. In Lincolnshire medieval documents show salt making was a seasonal occupation. In Kent there are probable medieval saltern mounds on the Isle of Sheppey, known locally as 'coterells'.

The Lymington salt flats on the Solent were important in the medieval period. Here brine was concentrated by solar evaporation before being boiled in lead open pans. King's Lynn and Boston salt was exported to Scotland along with cloth, and the first records of salting in the Tyneside area come from 1462 and 1489, referring to the earliest open pans made of iron, which were built at South Shields.

On the Lincolnshire coast the twelfth-century sleeching ('muldefang') process continued in use through the late medieval period until the Great Flood of 1571 destroyed many sites, which finally closed in the face of competition from imported bay salt. The remains of the sleeching process can still be seen in huge mounds, remnants of deposits cleared from the sleech pits.

Some 'sunworks' of the sixteenth and seventeenth centuries on the east coast used solar evaporation. A text from the reign of Charles I refers to the area of Caister-by-Yarmouth, Norfolk, where the saltmarsh 'is cut and formed into sunpans, channells, cesternes, conservatories, and many other workes for the seasonable receiving, purifying, separating and evaporating seawater, whereof we make salt without fewell. These works are made in the marsh ground subject to present inundation.'

In the north of England sleeching was carried out on the Solway Firth into the post-medieval period. The remains of a salt works with its kinches and houses can be seen at Crosscanonby, near Maryport, Cumbria. The process of brine concentration by sleeching was laborious but economised on the use of fuel. This site has been protected from further marine erosion and consolidated.

John Leland visited the coastline of the north-west of England in about 1535–43 and described salt making near Maryport: 'at the end of the sandes I saw divers salte cootes wher were divers hepes of sandys taken of salt strondys owt of which by often wettyng with water they pyke owt the saltines and so the water is derived into a pit and after sodde' [simmered]. Coal had been available to salt makers at Whitehaven and Maryport from the thirteenth century and in 1633 the Lowthers built salt pans near their coal mines at Whitehaven, copying iron salt pans at Newcastle.

After rock salt was discovered in 1670 at Marbury, Cheshire, other salt-making sites were adapted to use rock salt to strengthen seawater but the

The brine well on the beach at Crosscanonby, Cumbria, led brine to the kinch, where it was poured over the sleech and concentrated.

At Kimmeridge Bay, Dorset, Sir William Clavell of Smedmore, who owned the bay, established a short-lived salt works in 1610, where he used Kimmeridge shale as a fuel. The works was located on the east headland, just above the shoreline, below Clavell Tower.

number of such refineries was restricted by an Act of 1732.

Wind power was used on some coastal sites to pump brine from the sea to large cisterns. During the sixteenth and seventeenth centuries at Lymington windmills were used to fill large cisterns with brine, whence it flowed into open pans of lead. A patent granted by James I for the 'New Invention of Makinge of White and Bay Salt' (1625) caused some difficulty as it involved serious structural alterations. We hear that the greatest number of salters 'maketh brine in floore pannes after the new way, the residue after th'old way, and boyleth in one iron pann, and the

The windpump at Southwold, Suffolk, 1861. Southwold demonstrates the fluctuations in the sea salt industry. These were caused by changes in the coastline and influenced by taxation, changing demand for salt caused by the fortunes of the fishing industry, and developments in transport. Early salterns existed but were not present during the compilation of Domesday Book. Charles I issued a charter to Southwold Corporation permitting them to establish salt buildings and warehouses. The coat of arms from the salt tax office, 1673, has been incorporated into the gable of a new house. A warm seawater bath-house was erected from 1766, heated by waste heat from the salt pans, but salt making ended in 1894. Seawater was led into Salt Creek at high spring tides and was pumped by a windmill and hand pump through wooden troughs into three salt pans.

Saltmarshes between Lymington and Keyhaven, known simply and appropriately as 'The Salterns'. Here the grid of evaporating ponds is still visible.

Right: *Creek Cottage, Lymington. The building in the foreground is one of two believed to be the last remaining salt works buildings in the Lymington area. Their exact purpose is not known – perhaps they were storehouses rather than actual boiling houses. The water in the foreground provided access from the salt works to the Solent.*

rest in lead panns'. The Lymington industry took advantage of sales to America but by the nineteenth century was put in difficulties by the competition from the inland Cheshire salt manufacturers.

In Wales, on the Gower peninsula, a salt works at Port Eynon was in use between 1550 and 1650. The Aberdyfi salt works in Gwynedd was one of a number set up around the coast of England and Wales under a patent granted to Casper Seelar in 1564. These works were intended both to supply salt to the local herring fisheries and to make good supplies

The salt works at Lymington in Hampshire as they appeared about the 1830s, drawn by Edward King in later life from childhood memories.

The Salt House, Port Eynon, Gower, South Wales. Part of a sixteenth-century wooden lift pump was found in the pump chamber of the brine reservoir during excavations in advance of consolidation to protect the monument from erosion. (Crown copyright, RCAHMW: DI2006–0013)

from France interrupted by war. From the late seventeenth century Frodsham, Cheshire, in the port of Liverpool, was exporting increasing amounts of white salt and rock salt around the coast of Britain, and the coastal salt works of Wales became uneconomic and closed.

In Fife and Lothian, Scotland, coal replaced peat for making salt as early as the thirteenth century, the coal being too poor in quality for other uses. From 1575 George Bruce produced 90 tons of salt per week from forty-four pans at Culross. By 1614 salt was Scotland's third largest export after wool and fish, and of course the fish was salted as well. Tidal reservoirs or 'bucket pots' were built as stone-walled enclosures or as reservoirs cut into bedrock on the shore, buckets being used to transfer seawater into pans until pumps were introduced. Salt was made around the coast at sites such as Maryburgh, Prestwick, Ayrshire, the Cock of Arran and on the Calf of Eday, Orkney. At Annandale in

The Fife coastal survey identified salt-making sites and assessed the threats from coastal erosion. St Monans produced salt from cheap, poor local coal from 1790 to 1823. The site consists of rock-cut brine tanks (bucket pots), a windmill, sluices, nine pan houses and the connecting railway. This site used 8 tons of coal to make 1 ton of salt, compared to half a ton of coal to make 1 ton of salt in Cheshire.

The salt pans on the Calf of Eday, Orkney, were built in the seventeenth century to take advantage of its large peat reserves and its position near the fishing grounds. Twelve pans were erected about 1633 by the Earl of Carrick, but by 1672 only one pan was recorded in use. Two buildings now remain, with massive semicircular end walls and fireplace arches, but they are under threat of erosion by the sea. Extensive peat mounds are the remains of stacks to feed the fires.

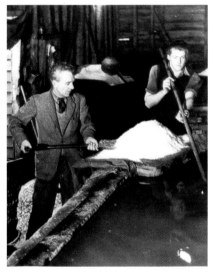

Dumfries and Galloway sleeching is known to have been the process used.

During the eighteenth century the salt makers of the Scottish west coast were under pressure because salt smuggled from Ireland was undercutting local prices. Production from seawater alone continued but after the abolition of the salt tax some producers survived the competition from cheap good quality Cheshire salt by going over to rock salt refining. The last works making salt from seawater alone, at Saltcoats, Ayrshire, closed in the late 1870s. A small number continued by refining rock salt in seawater to strengthen the brine. The works at Prestonpans did not close until 1959.

In Essex the Maldon Crystal Salt Company continues the tradition of open pan evaporation, producing large, flaked crystal salt on the Blackwater estuary. At Brynsiencyn on Anglesey sea salt is produced using water from the Menai Strait.

Above: *At Maldon, Essex, the process of evaporating brine in open pans to make crystal salt is still in operation, based on the exploitation of seawater from the Blackwater estuary. After concentration in lagoons, the brine is slowly simmered to develop hollow pyramidal salt crystals. This is the last open pan salt works in the United Kingdom. The photograph shows the late Cyril Osborne harvesting sea salt in the 1950s for his family business, the Maldon Crystal Salt Company.*

Right: *The Anglesey Sea Salt Company was started as a diversification at the Anglesey Sea Zoo, Brynsiencyn, and now makes a speciality Welsh salt. The seawater is drawn from the Menai Strait and concentrated by vacuum evaporation to reduce energy costs. It produces a saturated solution, which is then evaporated under lamps. The brine retains its natural mineral salts. The product is sold as 'Halen Môn'.*

Inland salt making

Early inland salt making was based on six areas of Triassic salt beds that stretch down the western side of England from Cumbria to Somerset. The Permian salt beds underlying Teesside are 365 metres (1200 feet) below the surface – too deep for brine springs to appear at the surface – and so the inland salt industry was based entirely on the exploitation of brine springs or pumped 'wild' brine from the Triassic beds until the mining of the salt beds began at Marbury, Cheshire, after 1670.

The largest area of salt beds in Britain underlies Cheshire, north Shropshire and Droitwich in Worcestershire. Here the early salt industry was centred on natural brine springs, along the river valleys. Salt was made in ceramic pots and salt pans and transported in ceramic containers (briquetage) over long distances.

Excavations at Droitwich uncovered first-century AD salt making at Friar Street and showed that hearths were in use into the fifth to seventh

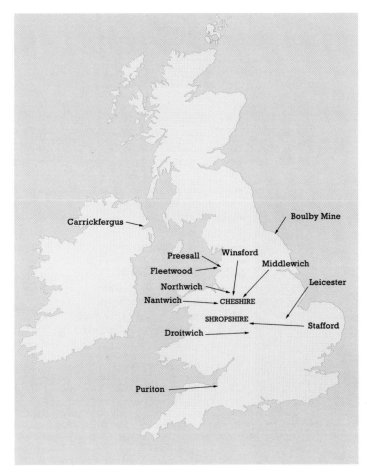

Areas and specific sites where rock salt has been exploited through natural brine springs, brine pumping or rock salt mining.

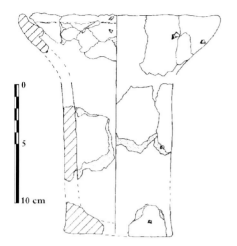

Above: *Specialist ceramics developed in different areas. This is an Iron Age briquetage container from Cheshire.*

Right: *A fifth- to seventh-century Anglo-Saxon hearth at Droitwich. This hearth would have been used to heat three lead pans set in a line, such as those illustrated on page 8. This is economical on fuel. The fire is set only at the front of the hearth, so the first pan is hot and the third pan is relatively cool.*

centuries in the Upwich area of the town. In Cheshire near Harbutts Field, Middlewich, and at Kingsley Field, Nantwich, archaeology has shown the industrial scale of Roman salt production. The discovery in Cheshire of lead salt pans with late Roman inscriptions linking salt production to the early Christian church has added to our knowledge of how the industry developed and was financed.

In the medieval period the white salt industry was put under pressure by competition from imported sea salt. However, the whiteness of inland salt made in lead pans (combined with the ability of skilled salt makers to produce differing grades of salt by altering the fires) ensured that it was preferred by many, particularly in butter and cheese making and for table use.

In Whitchurch, north Shropshire, salt was manufactured during the thirteenth century but

A recreation of salt making in a replica Roman lead salt pan at the Lion Salt Works Trust, Northwich. The salt-maker is being watched by the Ermine Street Guard. The hearth and tools are based on excavated examples found in Middlewich and Droitwich. The front lead pan is based on one discovered at Shavington, Cheshire. The brine used here is a saturated solution (25 per cent). Having been heated for about one hour, it is just starting to form salt.

Left: *Excavations in Middlewich and Nantwich have found ancient salt-making sites. Two large Roman brine tanks were excavated at Kingsley Field, Nantwich, in 2002. Their construction had been a huge feat of engineering. In shifting-sand, the Romans dug an enormous hole in which to construct the timber storage tanks. Each tank was lined with clay a metre (3 feet) thick on the outer sides to prevent fresh water seeping in and diluting the brine. The purple clay can be seen in the photograph, which also shows the effect of the freshwater springs.*

Right: *A medieval wich house was excavated at Great Wood Street, Nantwich, in 1980. The walls of the building were still preserved but no pans survived.*

The salt ship from Great Wood Street, Nantwich. Salt ships were hollowed-out tree trunks that were used as brine cisterns for individual wich houses. Two more salt ships have been discovered, each over 7 metres (23 feet) long.

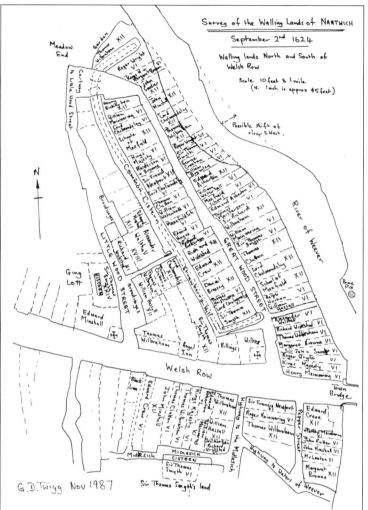

This is a copy by George Twigg of the seventeenth-century map of Nantwich showing wich houses. Similar maps exist for Northwich and Droitwich and give the names of the owners of individual wich houses.

the brine was weak and the works closed by the end of the eighteenth century.

The rock salt beds beneath the Stafford area provided wild brine supplies at Shirleywich and were exploited at the end of the seventeenth century. Stafford Common and Baswich salt works opened in the mid 1890s but claims for compensation arising from subsidence led to their closure in 1970. The short-lived Moira open pan salt works at Ashby-de-la-Zouch spa, Leicestershire, opened in 1837 but operated for less than twenty years.

Three areas of Droitwich – Netherwich, Middlewich and Upwich – were involved in the medieval salt industry. Like the Cheshire salt towns, Droitwich was the centre of a network of packhorse routes. New brine wells were opened in 1695, and in 1768 the opening of Brindley's canal

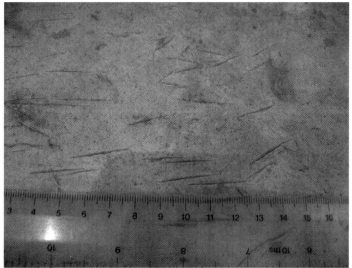

The physics and chemistry of evaporating brine were the same in the past as they are today. Pan scale builds up as natural brine is evaporated. If it is not removed, the scale will insulate the brine in the pan from the heat of the fire, decreasing the efficiency of the evaporation process and possibly causing lead pans to melt. In this detail from the Bostock pans (page 8), pick marks on the surface of a lead salt pan show the effects of the removal of pan scale.

provided a direct link with the River Severn, stimulating trade. The Droitwich salt industry reached its peak in 1872, with large open pan salt works, but closed in 1922.

A new brine source was discovered nearby at Stoke Prior, Worcestershire, by William Furnival in 1825 and a larger works than at Droitwich was built there, helped by William Gossage's improvement to the Le Blanc process for making soda in 1830. However, problems with brine supplies and poor management eventually led to the liquidation of the British

This photograph shows the massive size of the medieval brine well and pump which were excavated at Droitwich in 1983–4. The Upwich well was constructed in 1264–5. The timbers at the bottom left are Roman structures centred on the brine springs. In the medieval period the exploitation of brine was strictly controlled by the town authorities. Each town had its own regulations but they all aimed at sharing out the brine according to each person's entitlement. When the brine was taken out of the well it was transferred to the individual wich house through a series of wooden channels, which connected each wich house to the brine pit. In Northwich the channels ran along the ground. Blocking the channels was a punishable offence. The salt makers followed their allocation of brine as it ran from the well to the cistern. See page 53 for brine channels in use today at Salinas de Añana, Spain.

There have been many treatises on salt making. Domesday Book lists inland salt works and coastal salinas. Agricola described different methods of salt making in 'De Re Metallica', published in 1555, and Camden describes the wich towns in 1607. There are the 'Walling Books of Northwich', and William Smith's book 'Vale Royal' of 1656 describes the salt towns of Cheshire. William Jackson described the process used by Droitwich salt makers to the Royal Society in 1669 (right), followed by Dr Thomas Rastel in 1678. In 1746 Thomas Lowndes of Middlewich published a pamphlet 'for improving the making of salt from brine' directed to the Lords of the Admiralty and the College of Physicians. Two years later, in 1748, William Brownrigg published 'The Art of Making Salt'. In 1787 Christopher Chrysel, a German scientist, published a pamphlet emphasising the economical side of salt making, which was again covered in Henry Holland's 1808 publication 'The Production of Salt Brine'.

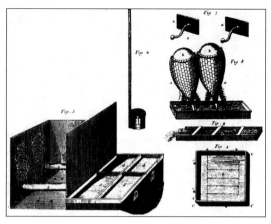

Alkali Company that had run the works. In 1852–5 John Corbett purchased the company for £33,000 and solved the problem of brine supply by lining the brine shaft with metal. He sold the works, which by then had incorporated Imperial Salt (bought for a further £24,000), to the Salt Union for £660,000 in 1888. In 1937 the works became part of ICI Salt Division and closed in 1973. As at Stafford, subsidence problems resulted from wild brine pumping.

On Teesside salt making based on the deeper Permian salt beds began in 1862 near Middlesbrough. Brine was pumped from the rock salt by the solution mining technique and salt was evaporated in open pans. It was used as a raw material for a developing alkali industry but most of the salt works had closed by the 1920s.

At Preesall, Lancashire, a bed of rock salt was discovered in 1872. Here the Fleetwood Salt Company, formed in 1883 and part of the United Alkali Company after 1890, mined rock salt (from 1893) and pumped brine through pipes under the River Wyre to an open pan salt works and an ammonia soda works at Fleetwood.

The salt industry was cyclical. A shortage of salt would either pull in imports from abroad or put up prices, and small producers had problems in stabilising prices. This variability led to new salt-making ventures springing up rapidly, only to fail when over-supply

Wicker baskets used to drain salt and make conical moulds were replaced in the nineteenth century by 'peg-top tubs', stave-built containers made by coopers, as shown here. In turn these were replaced by more easily made elm boxes. Not many survive, as they would have been burnt when broken or replaced by newer boxes. This example is from the Lion Salt Works, Northwich, Cheshire.

This working replica of a medieval salt works at Læsø, Denmark, produces different grades of salt. The salt crystals, which are just appearing on the surface of the iron pan, are known as 'fleur du sel' and are skimmed off the surface of the brine as they form. Large crystals are formed from slow, medium heat, fine crystals by boiling at higher temperatures. It takes great skill to harvest 'fleur du sel', which fetches a premium price.

brought prices down again. There had been attempts to control the price of salt, and the salt tax had to a degree protected some parts of the industry, particularly in Scotland and Ireland. Eventually a concentrated attempt was made to form a cartel of salt producers. The Salt Association was a forerunner in England of the Salt Union, formed in 1888. In 1889 the Scottish Salt Company was formed, based on similar lines to the Salt Union, being eventually wound up in 1964.

The Salt Union bought out salt works and closed down many smaller operations to centralise production and supply. Almost immediately there were problems. The Salt Union had paid too much for some works (such as Corbett's at Stoke Prior) and some proprietors took the money and used it to start new, 'modern' works in competition with the Union. At this period many overseas markets were secure because buyers were part of the British Empire, but as sales to America, Africa, India and Australia declined markets in the new chemical industries in the United Kingdom increased.

The Salt Union was eventually absorbed into Imperial Chemical Industries (ICI) in 1936 but salt making and brine pumping were divested from the parent company at the end of the 1990s, along with the rock salt mining and soda-ash businesses. Other salt businesses were likewise absorbed into chemical companies such as BP Chemicals and subsequently closed down or resold.

Since 1977 bulk white salt production has been confined to Cheshire

Developments by the United Alkali Company at Preesall, Lancashire, brought about the start of controlled brine pumping. The brine field well-heads and the mine-head buildings no longer survive.

with two white salt works using vacuum evaporators, at Middlewich and Weston Point, Runcorn, and a smaller vacuum works at Wincham. The larger plants source their brine by solution mining from controlled brine-pumping fields. The New Cheshire Salt Works at Wincham, a family-run concern, remained a 'wild brine' pumper but was bought by British Salt and closed in 2006 when the production of its pharmaceutical salt and water-softening products was transferred to Middlewich.

Salt is now manufactured in bulk for multi-national chemical and food companies and its production is influenced by global economics. However, hand-made salt is making a comeback: at Maldon it has never stopped. Sea salt making returned to Wales in 1998, on Anglesey, and new ventures are planned at Prestonpans in Scotland. At the Lion Salt Works in Northwich, Cheshire, the working of historic salt pans is demonstrated to the public and there are plans to build an open pan for the production of block salt as part of a working museum. In 2006 the Trust was awarded a grant of £4.96 million from the Heritage Lottery Fund to restore the surviving works as a heritage site.

Brine is still exploited for its health-giving properties at Droitwich Spa, Worcestershire, and at an open-air swimming pool at Nantwich, Cheshire.

The salt workers

According to Leland, in the sixteenth century salt making, or 'walling', was carried out by women. The salt pans at this time were small and so the weight of salt being raked and drawn was not very great. The work was hot and repetitive but the heavier tasks such as drawing brine from the well and collecting and preparing fuel were carried out by men. Working a salt pan was a family affair and this practice continued into the nineteenth century, although the factory inspectors disapproved of men with bare chests working alongside women dressed only in their underwear because of the heat.

In England and Wales salt makers were free to move as they wished but an Act of the Scottish Parliament of 1606 barred colliers and salt makers from moving to a new employer and in 1703 they were specifically excluded from the Scottish Habeas Corpus Act. Salt makers appeared in sale records of salt works, listed alongside the pans and warehouses. On the west coast of Scotland workers were often housed in rooms above the salt works themselves. Acts passed in 1775 and 1799 ended the practice of life binding for salt workers.

Changes in society and legislation ended contractual work whereby salt makers worked to produce given volumes of salt. Men became employed directly by owners and worked shifts of eight or twelve hours on a piecework system supervised by the proprietor and a foreman, aided by clerks.

There were differing jobs with varying degrees of skill. The most highly skilled salt makers were the *lumpmen*, who worked the hottest pans for

Cones of salt made in peg-top tubs at the Lion Salt Works, Marston, Northwich, Cheshire. These are a cooper's version of the wicker baskets excavated from medieval contexts in Droitwich. The empty tubs can be stacked inside one another to save space, something that could not be done with the later square elm tubs.

A salt warehouse with lumps made in peg-top tubs.

making blocks of salt in tubs using rakes and skimmers, happers and mundling sticks. *Wallers* raked common salt from pans while labourers shovelled the coarsest fishery salt for bulk loading in an undried state. *Lofters* were employed to move the dried blocks from the stove houses to the warehouses, where they were stacked before shipment as lumps or ground into crystals for packing into sacks.

    Raking crystals was the most dangerous job and men were often scalded or fell into pans, sometimes to their death. Wounds remained open, and though salt is an antiseptic ulcers formed and were slow to heal. Before sick pay was introduced, those who could no longer work in the pan houses were put on lighter duties, which often involved working in dirtier surroundings such as shovelling coal in the coal yards. Men and

Four salt workers, standing on hurdles beside an open pan, are raking, skimming, tubbing and happing salt. Happing squared up and smoothed down the lumps, which were to be sold as 'hand-it lumps'. Lumps that were to be crushed back to loose, fine crystals were left rough and after drying were moved by a spike, or prong, rather than by hand. The prong left a hole in the salt block, spoiling its appearance if being sold as a whole block.

Raking salt from an open pan while making 'broad' or coarse salt. As the brine is evaporated salt crystallises on the surface. As the crystals grow in weight and size, they sink to the bottom of the pan and are drawn to the side with long-handled rakes from each side of the pan. The waller, or salt maker, lifts the salt from the pan using a skimmer, allowing it to drain slightly before placing it on the hurdles behind him.

Mr Heath, the last lumpman at the Lion Salt Works, using a skimmer to fill salt tubs. The process is identical to earlier images but his skimmer is made from stainless steel and the tubs, or moulds, are made from glass-fibre.

Below: Skimmers are perforated scoops that allow brine to drain through. Stainless steel skimmers were not liked, as they remained heavy through their life. Iron skimmers lost weight as they rusted and, like scythes, were thought to be at their best just before they disintegrated.

Left: Elm salt tubs, a mundling stick (front left) and a happer (front right). The tubs and mundling stick are made of elm, a wood with twisted grain, enabling them to withstand the saturated hot brine. The happers are made of beech, and so, like butter pats, they too could withstand the brine. These examples are replicas used in Lion Salt Works demonstration days. Even though they have been cleaned, notice how salt crystallises out of the wood. A supply of fresh water for cleaning tools while working was essential to prevent salt crystals forming on tool handles, abrading both hands and wood.

32

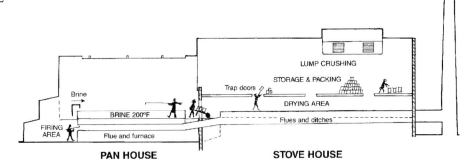

PAN HOUSE **STOVE HOUSE**

Above: *Cross-section through an open pan salt works. Although much bigger, it is essentially the same as a sixteenth-century salt works. It is divided into two sections, a pan house and a stove house. The firing area is sheltered by a 'caboose', a simple lean-to roof that also covers the 'forby', the brickwork surrounding the fire doors and the ash holes at the stoking area end of the open pans. The caboose was often outside the main roofline of the*

pan house. The pan has a simple roof to keep the weather from it but is well ventilated to allow steam vapour to escape. Salt was wheeled from the pan for drying in the brick stove house before being 'lofted' to the warehouse above ready for packing and delivering to customers. The waste heat from the furnace was ducted below the drying area (the stove or hot house, or 'otters'). The rate coal was burnt was regulated by dampers at the end of the pan and the base of the chimney.

Above: *An aerial view of the Lion Salt Works, Marston, Northwich, Cheshire. The Lion Salt Works was the last traditional inland open pan salt works and closed in 1986. The Lion Salt Works Trust is working to preserve this scheduled monument. It was built where the Northwich to Warrington road crossed the Trent & Mersey Canal.*

Right: *The fires under the pans at the Lion Salt Works were converted to use recycled engine oil as cheap coal became hard to obtain and fuel costs rose steeply in the 1970s.*

Salt pans needed to be raised to repair damaged pan plates and to remove the build-up of soot and ash in the furnace and flues. The raising procedure required the use of a 'jigger tool', whereby a gang of men raised and lowered the jigger arm, walking the pegs up the jigger leg. The jigger tool is attached to a ring and hook fixed to the side of the pan. The bottom plates of open pans need to be replaced every six months.

children fell down unfenced boreholes and mine shafts, were crushed beneath salt pans during riveting work, fell into crushing mills or drowned in the canals.

Salt works needed other skills, too: they employed their own blacksmiths, carpenters and joiners, who mended the pans and made the tools used at the works. Firing up the pans, which measured at least 9 metres (about 30 feet), was a job for a specialist, who might be responsible for firing more than one pan. A lumpman sometimes did this job, to have control of his own pan, but more usually the

Above: The brick flues from the pans run through the stove house to the chimney. The stove house is built of brick to retain heat. Salt lumps were placed between and on top of the flues to dry. It took fourteen days to dry a lump, during which time it was moved from the ditch to the top of the flue. From here the lumps were lofted to the warehouse above.

The warehouse was built over the stove house as a second floor, using the rising heat to keep the salt dry. Lumps were stored here and ground up if necessary before dispatch.

The 'Coronation' salt store at the Lion Salt Works was built in 1901. Its external framing is similar to the description of the sixteenth-century storehouse at the Aberdyfi salt works in Gwynedd, Wales. The construction details record that 'a howse be made to keep salt in, walls and floore whereof on the yner side must be boarded to keep the salt from the earth'.

A stencil denoting a factory-filled sack to be shipped by Paterson Zochonis, a shipping agent exporting salt to West Africa from Liverpool and Manchester.

fireman's sole duties were the firing, maintenance and cleaning of his pans. The blacksmith also shod the horses. Bricklayers and other building tradesmen were employed full-time repairing pan houses and maintaining the offices. Casual labourers were called in as needed, the children of foremen being used as runners to fetch men, sometimes for only one or two hours work. These men loaded and unloaded the coal and stencilled labels on the tens of thousands of bags used at each works. Different orders would require cotton, hessian or double-wefted sacks until pre-printed polypropylene became dominant in modern times.

Cotton sacks were printed with the emblems of the various companies, each easily identifiable without requiring translation into different languages. Cotton was popular, particularly in Africa, where the bags were washed and reused, avoiding duty levied on imported cotton.

*Before automation,
the packing of salt
was carried out by
women. Blocks of salt
were wrapped in
waxed paper.*

Women sewed sacks by hand, producing characteristic 'ears' that allowed the sacks to be lifted for hand loading. Hand sewing continued until the introduction of machine stitching and the mechanisation of loading by pallet and fork-lift trucks.

Ancillary trades depended on salt works for business. These included haulage firms for the supply and distribution of fuel and the removal and disposal of waste products such as clinker and scale, as well as for the carriage of the finished product from the works to customers, either by packhorse, wagon, barge, narrowboat, railway wagon or lorry.

When fuel changed from wood to coal, local residents complained vociferously about air pollution. As production increased, conditions deteriorated. The *Manchester Guardian* in 1888 reported: 'Every blade of grass in the vicinity is being killed off, and hillsides and fields are reduced to bare surfaces of baked clay.' In 1887 29,000 tons of sulphur dioxide was emitted from salt-works chimneys.

Salt makers found it hard to get warm at home because of the extreme heat and humidity inside the pan houses where they worked, and the constant change in temperature between work and home is thought to have led to chest complaints. The harsh conditions often led to men drinking large amounts of beer or ale to quench their thirst at the end of each shift and there are several accounts of deaths by falling into the canal as a result of a combination of fatigue and alcohol. Some proprietors promoted temperance but salt making had been associated with drinking since the medieval period, when brine drawers at Northwich town well were fined for drunkenness.

Many families scavenged for cinders from the cinder heaps around salt works in the winter months. In a domestic fireplace the cinders, or 'bass', would last a long time and hold the heat. Air pollution in salt-making areas was trapped around the towns and the works, which were situated in valleys. It was, however, possible to reach the countryside by walking less than a mile, which many workers did on Sundays.

Salt refining

Initially salt refining was a means of combating the trade in cheap but contaminated sea salt, which was imported from the Bay of Bourgneuf. As late as the eighteenth century complaints were made that French sea salt was contaminated and that herring salted with it went off. People also complained that the seawater was not filtered before entering the salinas. This failure to cure herring could have been caused by a build-up of bitter magnesium salts in the sea salt as a result of lack of care in making the salt. These bitter salts retard the effect of sodium chloride so that curing is incomplete and the fish go bad.

It was discovered that by re-dissolving the sea salt in clean seawater and then evaporating the resulting strong brine by the open pan method the bitter salts would remain behind. Thus clean white salt suitable for curing fish was produced more cheaply than by evaporating seawater alone.

On Tyneside from the fourteenth century salt was made in iron pans using poor quality, cheap coal. The resulting salt was often black or grey. This salt was sent to the east coast refineries to be remade into white salt.

When rock salt was discovered at Marbury, Cheshire, in 1670 it was used in refineries in the Liverpool Bay area, such as the Dungeon at Hale and on Hilbre Island. Under the terms of the Salt Tax Act of 1694 a bushel of rock salt weighed 120 pounds (54 kg) whereas a bushel of white salt weighed 56 pounds (25 kg), thereby making the tax on rock salt almost half that of white salt. Marl and sand are present in rock salt, but not as much as 50 per cent. From this time large quantities of rock salt began to be shipped around the coast to refineries from Frodsham, on the River Weaver but in the Port of Liverpool. Even though the tax on rock

An important use of salt was for preserving fish. All kinds of fish were salted, notably herring, which has to be salted within twenty-four hours of being caught.

salt was gradually raised, it remained lower than that on white salt. However, Acts of Parliament in 1702 and 1732 limited the number of works licensed to refine rock salt and this caused many to close and prevented new businesses from starting up.

The salt refineries were widely distributed but short-lived. A principal feature was the large steeping tanks (or salt ponds), fed by pipes or gutters with seawater, in which rock salt was dissolved to form a strong brine.

Coal reserves between Maryport and Whitehaven in Cumbria were exploited in the seventeenth century, leading to the establishment of a salt-refining industry in that area, because coal made it possible to heat larger pans than was feasible by burning peat and turf as the earlier north Cumbrian industry did.

In 1686 letters patent were granted to John Wilkes, giving him the privilege of making 'white salt' in the ports of King's Lynn and Boston on the Wash and at Hull, as well as at his principal works at Sunderland. He sent boats south from Sunderland laden with coal and they returned carrying salt.

In the north-east of England a number of sites refined sea salt using open pans fired by coal from South Shields and Tynemouth, and this became one of the most important industries in the area during the seventeenth century. Dirty salt from here was exported to Colchester, Essex, for 'salt-on-salt' refining. Other refineries were developed after 1670 on the east coast of England from Northumberland to the Humber, including sites at Hull and Sunderland, using Cheshire rock salt, but by 1785 only twenty pans were in operation. Salt works at South Shields continued longer, with several shown on the first edition of the Ordnance Survey map, c.1858.

In the south-east most of the Suffolk saltings became salt refineries. The Southwold works, dating from 1614, originally used salt from Spain or the Cape Verde Islands. Essex refineries at Manningtree, Goldhanger and Heybridge, using rock salt from Cheshire, were still in use in 1819. At Heybridge a squarish mound, 26 by 32 metres (85 by 105 feet), with the south side some 3–5 metres (10–16 feet) high, stands on a marsh known as Salt Court and on the stretch of river known as Colliers' Reach.

Pennys Lane Mine, Northwich. Note the second shaft on the right and the person being conveyed into the mine in the large salt tub, which would also be used to raise the rock salt to the surface. Mines were constructed with sumps to drain water, which might otherwise dissolve the bottom of the rock salt pillars left to support the roof of the mine. Pennys Lane Mine, Barons Quay Mine and Witton Hall Mine were flooded with brine when they were worked out. A programme to fill these voids with pulverised flue ash, salt and cement is now underway to prevent the collapse of Northwich town centre.

Rock salt mining

Rock salt mining is associated with those inland areas that have a long history of pumping brine and it led to the development of the coastal salt-refining industry described in the previous chapter.

Rock salt was first discovered while prospecting for coal in 1670 at Marbury near Northwich, approximately 45 metres (148 feet) below ground. Mining commenced within a few years, but there were many

Five cast-iron shaft-lining sections from a Marston mine were salvaged by the Lion Salt Works Trust during the capping of old shafts carried out by Cheshire County Council. The sections have riveted seams with male-to-female sockets and are bolted together with external rods, bolts and flanges. Earlier shafts are described as being timber-lined and well puddled. Keeping water from seeping into rock salt mines was of paramount importance.

problems due to the proximity of brine streams in the 'wet rock head' areas. Early mines were left with insufficiently large pillars to support the weight of marl above and mines collapsed, leaving huge areas of subsidence.

In 1777 the lower bed of dry rock salt at Lawton, Cheshire, was discovered by boring. John Gilbert dug through the sole of his Marston Top Mine in Northwich to the dry rock salt and used a Boulton & Watt steam engine to raise rock salt and pump brine in 1780/1. After this all mines in the Northwich area were sunk directly to the bottom bed at 90 metres (295 feet).

Rock salt was found at Stoke Prior in 1829, Winsford in 1844, Carrickfergus, Northern Ireland, in 1851 and Middlesbrough in 1863.

In 1889 rock salt was discovered at 90 metres (295 feet) at Walney Island, Cumbria, and the Barrow Salt Company was formed in 1896 but closed shortly after 1909. Rock salt mining at Fleetwood started in 1893 and peaked in 1906 but subsidence problems there caused the mine to close in the 1920s.

At Puriton, Somerset, rock salt was discovered at a depth of 198 metres (650 feet) when drilling for coal in 1910, but the Dunball Salt Works closed in 1922. The Adelaide Mine at Marston, Northwich, flooded in 1928, after which production moved to the Meadowbank Mine at Winsford.

At the Meadowbank Mine, Winsford, the covered conveyor belt, which delivers crushed rock salt to the cone-shaped loading shed, allows crushed rock salt to be processed without the wind spreading salt dust to surrounding land. Crushed rock salt is piled alongside, ready to be loaded into trucks. The marl in the rock salt is exposed on the surface of the pile. This stops the rain dissolving the salt, a property known as 'self thatching'.

No. 3 shaft at the Meadowbank Mine, Winsford, Cheshire, on the west bank of the River Weaver. This mine was first sunk in 1844, working on a small scale until 1892. It was reopened by the Salt Union in 1928 following the collapse of the Adelaide Mine at Marston. It became part of ICI in 1937 and expanded with new shafts in 1940 and 1963. It is currently operated by the Salt Union.

At the time of publication there are three rock salt mines in the United Kingdom: Meadowbank Mine, Winsford, Cheshire; the salt and potash mine at Boulby in North Yorkshire; and the Carrickfergus mine in Northern Ireland.

Above: *Rock salt samples from Winsford. Halite can be heavily contaminated by wind-blown sand and marl, or virtually pure clear sodium chloride. The banded layered sample demonstrates that deposits are laid down strati-graphically. This type of rock salt is crushed and used for de-icing the roads in the winter or for spreading on arable crops such as sugar beet. Rock salt for use at the table is imported from Germany to the United Kingdom.*

Modern workings at the Meadowbank Mine, Winsford: continual boring machines crush rock salt at the rock face and it is then brought to the surface along conveyors and up lift shafts.

The British Salt vacuum salt works, Middlewich, on the Trent & Mersey Canal. The blue tanks are used to purify the incoming brine before it enters the vacuum evaporators.

Vacuum salt works

The opening of the Salt Union's first commercial vacuum evaporator at Winsford, Cheshire, in 1905 was a turning point in the industry. Vacuum evaporation had been known about by Liverpool sugar refiners since 1813 and the salt industry experimented with single-effect evaporators at Shirleywich, Stafford, in 1889 and Winsford in 1901.

By 1912 the Salt Union had two vacuum plants and other manufacturers had three. Initially the vacuum plants could make only fine salt but by the late 1940s granular salt and dendritic salt were made by vacuum evaporation. In the face of this competition inland open pan salt works started to close.

Multiple-effect brine evaporators at British Salt, Middlewich, Cheshire. In the multiple-effect evaporators the same steam can heat six chambers in sequence or in parallel. Corrosion-resistant materials such as stainless steel and monel metal (a nickel-copper alloy) are used and usually the brine is purified before evaporation, creating pure sodium chloride, without the natural minerals that are found in sea salts, and natural brine, evaporated in an open pan.

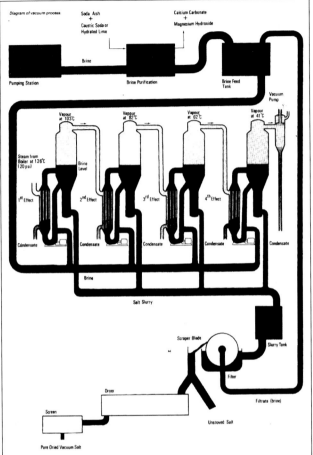

Diagram of vacuum process

Diagrammatic view of four effect evaporators connected in series. Brine is supplied from the brine field and purified before being fed to the evaporators. The brine in the first vessel is boiled at 103 degrees in the first effect evaporator but at only 41 degrees in the fourth effect evaporator. Salt is extracted via either a rotary filter or a centrifuge and dried in a fluid-bed drier.

Company and brand names became important for selling table salt to the public, and its free-running quality, unaffected by damp and storage, became prominent in the advertising of products such as Cerebos, Sifta and Saxa. Today vacuum salt works purify their brine and minute quantities of sodium hexacyanoferrate are added to enable the crystals to be taken out of the chambers as a slurry through a centrifuge. If the salt is to be sold as a table salt, magnesium carbonate is added to help its free-flowing characteristics.

Effects on the landscape

Areas that exploited salt on a large scale – principally Northwich (Cheshire), Droitwich (Worcestershire), Preesall (Lancashire) and Stafford – had some problems with ground movement and subsidence. Northwich was where the subsidence was most dramatic. Here the problems were exacerbated by the fact that two beds of rock salt were exploited. Each caused its own ground stability problems.

Rock salt mines are enormous caverns 10 metres (30 feet) deep, with pillars of rock salt left to support the roof of the mine. However, in the early period these pillars were only a small fraction of the size left by the modern practice, whereby at least as much is left standing as is taken out.

As some of the early mines became worked out they were deliberately flooded to produce 'bastard brine' to meet the increasing demand for brine required by the growing chemical industry. The result of all this was catastrophic. Fresh water entered mines, which were interconnected by adits and pipes, eroding the surviving rock salt pillars and causing enormous collapses. Random, migrating voids rose up from the salt deposits, creating localised swallow-holes, forming lakes in the countryside and causing buildings in the towns to collapse.

The first response was to try to keep buildings level and upright. To do this, shipbuilders were called in to jack up affected buildings. Gradually a tradition of framed buildings evolved, creating structures that were

Ashton's and Neumann's Flash, between Northwich town centre and the Trent & Mersey Canal, was formed as the result of the collapse of interlinked rock salt mines in the 1880s, shown here in a contemporary photograph. The collapse breached the River Weaver, causing it to flow backwards as it filled up the resulting subsidence hole. Preachers visited and preached repentance to the people who came to see the collapse.

Ashton's and Neumann's Flash Nature Park. The collapse eventually filled with rainwater and then was filled with lime waste. Now it is home to rare wildlife and has been colonised by orchids, which appreciate the poor but lime-rich soil, the by-product of the salt and chemical industry. This area is now open as a country park.

Below: Subsidence also happened in the countryside, miles away from the rock salt mines and brine pumping. At the point where the brine is pumped it is a saturated solution and little or no erosion occurs. However, solutioning of the rock salt occurs all along the path of the brine stream. As one moves further away from the extraction point so more fresh water is pulled over the rock salt and the rock head dissolves more quickly. Now a fishing pool, this freshwater pond has formed a linear feature along a brine stream formerly drawn into Middlewich, Cheshire.

Right: The collapse of the Marston Hall Mine in 1907 caused a major breach of the Trent & Mersey Canal (left). John Gilbert's Old Mine posed further problems, being a top-bed mine over a bottom-bed mine, and in the 1950s a new cut was made, diverting the canal to the north. Shortly after the cut was completed, the top-bed mine collapsed.

Left: Timber-framed buildings, Northwich. The first recorded house to be jacked was of brick. Eventually a system of subsidence-resistant timber-framed buildings was devised, whereby lightweight buildings were constructed with box frames, infilled with brick. Although still remaining on their medieval footprint, the Northwich buildings were rebuilt in this manner, and framed buildings eventually replaced brick buildings in the town centre. These were jacked and lifted, and the roads raised as required. Note the large beams placed underneath the building.

Detail of framing and internal boarding exposed during conservation work repairing the manager's office at the Lion Salt Works. Built c.1900, the building has a box frame with vertical studding filled with brick nogging. To keep the weight down, the inside walls were not plastered but clad in vertical tongue-and-groove boarding. In some buildings the internal boarding was laid diagonally to give additional strengthening.

resistant to subsidence. Framed buildings replaced damaged brick buildings and these were lifted as the ground continued to sink. The last 'big lift' of buildings was carried out in the 1960s. After that date only the Lion Salt Works and the New Cheshire Salt Works were pumping wild brine, the Northwich mines had all closed and been deliberately flooded with brine, and subsidence had almost ceased.

There were so many brine pumpers in the nineteenth century that it was impossible to attribute blame for subsidence to any particular proprietor. There was a long struggle to win compensation from the brine pumpers and in 1891 the first Brine Compensation Act was passed. This made provision for brine pumpers to pay a levy into a fund to be administered by the Brine Board and for compensation to be paid to claimants. The Board and compensation scheme still operate today.

A transfer to controlled brine pumping by ICI and British Salt through solution mining has been adopted in Cheshire, rapidly reducing subsidences. Within the 'brine fields' controlled brine pumping now provides saturated brine to Middlewich, Northwich and Runcorn from a series of wellheads and developed rock salt cavities.

Wellheads pump water into the rock salt cavities and distribute the brine to the vacuum salt works at Middlewich and Weston Point.

This packhorse bridge is one of three that cross the River Gowy, near Tarvin, Cheshire. This would have been a route used by salters carrying their product from the wich towns of Cheshire to the port of Chester.

Transport

Trade routes spread out from all the centres of salt production. Saltersford, Saltersway and Saltersbridge are names found along these routes. Early salt traders could be lone pedlars carrying salt on their backs to isolated areas or merchants with boats, wagons or strings of packhorses. Even heavily laden, a string of packhorses could travel along roads and across terrain impassable to wagons.

Droitwich sent salt up and down the River Severn and used the ports of Bristol and Gloucester. Cheshire salt was exported through the ports of Chester, Frodsham and Liverpool. While sea salt makers had their own hinterlands for distribution inland, they also sent their salt along the

Loading narrowboats with bulk salt on the Trent & Mersey Canal. The salt barrow, top left, tipped salt directly into the narrowboat. So much salt was spilt in this way that the canal became sufficiently saline to affect the buoyancy of boats. Steersmen had to take this into account when loading if they were passing through to fresh water beyond.

Weaver flats were used to transport salt down the River Weaver to docks in the Port of Liverpool. The coming of steam power and iron hulls allowed them to tow dumb barges. The 'Nautilus' (left) was owned by the Thompson family. At the end of her life her winch went to their Lion Salt Works to haul railway wagons on their private siding. Part of her mast was used to make a derrick over a borehole and these still survive there. These flats were also used for works outings on the River Weaver.

coast around Britain. There was a large and complex river- and sea-borne trade in the carriage of British and imported salt.

The growing importance of the Cheshire salt industry led to the opening of the Weaver Navigation and salt exported through the port of Liverpool was known everywhere as 'Liverpool salt'.

Salt was important as a ballast cargo and had a ready market at any destination. It was used as a back cargo to defray the cost of outward journeys made primarily to bring back other valuable goods. This lowered the cost of transported salt so that it distorted the markets and made imported salt cheaper than home-made both inside the United Kingdom and overseas. In this way all kinds of people were involved in the salt trade without participating in its manufacture.

Inland bulk cargoes gradually moved to the canals and then to the railways. Most salt works were connected to the railways early on, the salt

Above: *Railway salt vans were constructed with pitched roofs to help keep the salt cargo dry. These are now rare. A van survives, painted in Saxa livery, as part of the Great Western Railway collection. The iron straps were located on the outside to protect them from the salt. The example at the Lion Salt Works has signwriting from Chance & Hunt Ltd and the Salt Union. It finished its working life at the ICI Lostock Works, Northwich.*

Modern pure dried vacuum salt is delivered by specialist tankers.

Loading lorries with crushed rock salt at the Meadowbank Mine, Winsford, Cheshire, for distribution to gritting depots around Britain.

Right: *Rock salt piled by the side of the road, ready for collection by gritters in the winter at Cerrigydrudion, Conwy, North Wales.*

Left: *Sheep are attracted to bins of rock salt beside the road (here in the Lake District). Drovers used the attraction of animals for salt to control the lead cow while droving herds to market. The drover would hold salt in his hand and allow the lead animal to taste it. It would then follow him to get more licks of the salt.*

being carried in special vans with pitched roofs.

Specialist lorries now transport bulk cargoes of vacuum salt. Crushed rock salt is mainly used to keep roads free of ice in winter. Lorries deliver crushed rock salt from Meadowbank Mine in Winsford to depots around Britain for dispersal across the roads by gritting lorries.

The salt tax

For England and Wales the first Act of Parliament that taxed salt at the point of manufacture was passed in 1694 and was initially intended to provide money for the wars of William III. It was briefly repealed between 1730 and 1732 but then continued until 1825. In Scotland salt taxes were integrated with those for the rest of Britain from 1707 and, as in England and Wales, had a higher rate imposed on imported salt, to act as a protection for native salt makers.

The tax was collected by salt revenue officers, who were appointed, employed and paid for by the Salt Office. Salt revenue officers were stationed at salt works, at ports to collect tax from imported foreign salt, at fishing villages and inland wherever salt was traded. The salt officers in England worked twenty-four hours on and twenty-four hours off. By day they weighed the salt out with their own scales and by night they kept a watch for smuggling. In Scotland, though, there were complaints that the revenue men kept office hours and as salt making went on round the clock stealing from the works at night was made easy. The officers were stationed away from areas in which they had grown up and were moved every four years to stop them becoming friendly with local people.

Before the Act of Union between England and Scotland in 1707 Scotland taxed salt from Ireland, England and Wales as foreign salt in order to protect its home industry. Salt makers on the Firth of Forth were anxious to protect their markets from Cheshire salt in particular. Salt from Cheshire, without taxation but including the high cost of transport, was reckoned to be cheaper brought to the doors of the Forth salt works than the salt that was made inside them. Salt was the eighth article out of twenty-five to be agreed before the Act of Union took place. On Tyneside salt makers used similar methods to those of the Scottish salt works on the Forth, and they had similar pre-tax costs and competed in the same markets overseas. The tax advantages that Scotland negotiated were cited by contemporaries as a reason for the decline in the Tyneside industry at this period.

Although salt was taxed 'in perpetuity', the Acts and regulations were continually updated and changed. Between 1760 and 1817 alone thirty Salt Acts were passed, some with over one hundred clauses, representing three hundred additional pages on the statute book.

As the tax was paid at the salt works, at first great financial strain was put on the salt proprietors at a time when banking was in its infancy and debtors could and did go to jail. Eventually small owners ceased trading and salt making was concentrated in the hands of a few wealthy proprietors, who feared that repeal of the Salt Tax Acts would open up salt making to small makers again. It was also claimed that the tax held back innovation because improvements in manufacture could have decreased the revenue derived from salt or coal.

The tax on salt increased gradually but in 1798 the tax on white salt was increased to 10 shillings a bushel and in 1805 to 15 shillings a bushel, a taxation rate of about 1500 per cent. Under the Acts there were 'drawbacks', or tax rebates, on salt for export and the fishing industry. By the end of the eighteenth century this extended to salt used in agriculture and the bleaching and chemical industries.

The Salt Tax Acts spread taxation into the lives of everyone, rich or poor, and so smuggling became rife. Salt was smuggled from the salt works and on the dockside in men's trousers and under women's petticoats, as well as by the shipload. Rock salt was smuggled to Ireland, where the tax was lower. It came back as Irish white salt, a product itself smuggled to the west coast of Scotland and to Wales for the herring fisheries. Salt for export was shipped out of port in broad daylight, having claimed the tax rebate, and then smuggled, or 'run back', at night, the ship having sailed barely over the horizon.

Smuggling a bulk cargo such as salt required good organisation and the salt revenue officer's job could be dangerous as salt smuggling was connived at even by Justices of the Peace. In a well-reported case from Conwy, North Wales, on 17th January 1712 a revenue officer was captured on the sand dunes as he spied on smugglers unloading salt. After pleading for his life he was held captive for two days in the hen house of the local magistrate, who was the leader of the gang. He could do nothing afterwards because of the position many gang members held in society.

When fish and meat were salted for use at sea double the normal amount of salt was supposed to be used because the extra salt was thought to prevent scurvy, but complaints were made that sufficient salt was never used, the extra salt being smuggled away.

Despite widespread smuggling, native salt was not held in bonded warehouses until the Act of 1798. Under the same Act people who sold salt had to be licensed for a fee and had to erect a board over their premises with their name and licence on it.

The mass of regulations and rules brought in to combat smuggling, combined with the high rate of the tax, caused problems. The west coast Scottish herring fisheries were not alone in complaining that because of regulations salt arrived from the bonded stores too late to be used. Either the shoals of fish had moved on or, if caught, the fish went bad before the salt arrived. Areas known for dry-curing bacon, such as Wiltshire, also complained about the difficulties of getting salt because of the regulations. Elsewhere the complaint was that the cost of salt and the cost of the regulations meant that inferior, cheaper products such as Dutch cheese were being bought in preference to British-made produce.

The salt tax was seen as a tax that affected the poor disproportionately, as the well-off ate more fresh food and the poor ate more salted food such as salt mutton, salt beef, salt pork, salted fish and cheese.

The movement for repeal brought together people otherwise politically dissimilar such as Sir Thomas Bernard, the social reformer, Colonel John Calcraft, MP for Wareham, Dorset, and the radical William Cobbett. The depression that followed the end of the Napoleonic Wars in 1815 delayed the repeal of the tax but eventually such pressure was brought on the government that in 1822 it was first announced that Scottish salt taxes would be repealed from January 1823 and the English and Irish salt tax much reduced. Further pressure led to the announcement on 2nd July 1822 that the Salt Tax Acts would be repealed for the rest of the United Kingdom with full effect from January 1825.

Glossary

Bastard brine: brine pumped from storage ponds created in worked-out underground rock salt mines.

Bay salt: large crystals from screened fishery salt. In a more general sense it could relate to open pan salt which matched the traditional French sea salt or bay salt from the Biscay coast.

Bitter salts: salts such as calcium sulphate are more soluble than sodium chloride and remain in solution within the brine pan. The build-up of such soluble impurities in the brine mother liquor was an important reason why the brine remaining in the pan at the end of each week was drained to waste. The salts have a bitter taste and in Germany were described as being like 'horse piss'.

Brine stream, spring: brine streams occur where rock salt (halite) is close to the surface and comes in contact with groundwater. The water flowing over the rock salt dissolves it, so forming brine streams. The brine streams may come to the surface through faults as brine springs.

Controlled brine pumping: the deliberate formation of dome-shaped cavities in rock salt deposits by the solution mining of the deposits through the pumping of fresh water into the cavity and forcing saturated brine back to the surface.

Dendritic salt: a vacuum salt made with a crystal-modifying agent to produce crystals which may be porous, star-shaped modified cubes with unique physical properties. Initially used to replicate open pan salt.

Granular salt: vacuum salt comprising spherical crystals of a coarse grain size and very high purity.

Hap: a horse-drawn device for raking up shore sand for use in sleeching.

Happer: a wooden tool, made of beech or willow, for smoothing the sides of lump salt after it was turned out of the tub but before the lumps are dried, in order to produce a 'handit' or handed lump.

Hopper crystals: salt crystals which have formed as inverted hollow quadratic pyramids with step-like sides. These form on the surface of undisturbed brine, sinking deeper as they grow, creating the hollow pyramidal shape.

Kinch: a pit lined with puddled clay into which air-dried sleech was put. It was prepared for use by spreading layers of straw or rushes over the floor and side to act as filters. It was connected to a cistern where the brine was collected. When all the salt was out of the sleech the kinch was emptied and refilled with fresh sleech.

Muldefang: an east coast term for strengthening seawater by a process similar to sleeching.

Mundling stick: a stick made of elm and used to compress salt crystals in salt tubs, forcing out excess brine.

Pan scale: scale deposited on the heated bottom plates of an open pan during the evaporation of natural brine. Essentially it was formed from the calcium, magnesium and sulphate present in the brine, and equivalent to the scale formed with hard water. Pan scale also contains salt. It built up rapidly in a boiling fine pan and could become an inch or two (25–50 mm) thick by the end of one week.

PDV: a dried vacuum salt, marketed under the initials, which stand for Pure Dried Vacuum salt.

Red Hill: a specific term referring to a type of site known only from the Essex area in the Roman period. The term is used to describe mounds of burnt, reddish-coloured earth containing briquetage.

Salt works: a complex of features for the making of salt, varying in size and techniques, and containing many components. This term is more applicable to small to large-scale industrial plants of the seventeenth and later centuries and may be used for coastal works where open pans are used for the main evaporation process.

Saltern: a complex of features for the extraction of salt from seawater, varying in size and techniques, but generally earlier than the seventeenth century. See *Salt works*.

Sleech: shore sand impregnated with salt, obtained from below the high-water line.

Sleeching: the process whereby sleech is put into a kinch and washed with seawater to obtain brine stronger than seawater. When the brine was strong enough to float an egg (16 per cent solution) it was boiled in open pans to produce white salt.

Solution mining: the deliberate pumping of water into rock salt deposits to dissolve the salt.

Wet rock head: where natural groundwater flows over the surface of rock salt deposits dissolving the salt to form underground brine streams.

Wild brine pumping: extraction of brine from underground brine streams. The brine is created naturally by the dissolution of rock salt by groundwater but is drawn more quickly than by the natural flow, producing larger volumes of brine.

Salt manufacturers, packers and distributors

Vacuum salt manufacturers

The Salt Manufacturers Association comprises the main United Kingdom salt-making companies: British Salt Ltd, Cheshire; Salt Union, Cheshire; Ineos Industries and Ineos Chlor, Cheshire; Cleveland Potash; Irish Salt & Mining Exploration Co Ltd, Carrickfergus, Northern Ireland. Website: www.saltsense.co.uk

Sea salt manufacturers

Anglesey Sea Salt Company, Anglesey Sea Zoo, Brynsiencyn, Llanfair PG, Anglesey LL61 6TQ. Website: www.seasalt.co.uk

Maldon Crystal Salt Company Ltd, Wycke Hill Business Park, Maldon, Essex CM9 6UZ. Website: www.maldonsalt.co.uk

Packers and distributors

Centura Foods Ltd. Website: www.rhm.co.uk/rhm/divisions/culinarybrands

Dripak Ltd, Derbyshire. Website: www.dripak.co.uk

J. C. Peacock Ltd. Website: www.peacocksalt.com

The salt-packing plant alongside the British Salt works at Middlewich is part of the RHM group.

Further reading

de Brisay, K., and Evans, K. A. (editors). *Salt: The Study of an Ancient Industry.* Colchester Archaeological Group, 1975.

Fawn, A. J.; Evans, K. A.; McMaster, I.; and Davies, G. M. R. *The Red Hills of Essex: Salt-making in Antiquity.* Colchester Archaeological Group, 1990.

Fielding, A. M., and Fielding, A. P. *Open Pan Salt Making in Cheshire, A Memoir by Tom Lightfoot.* Research Report No. 1, Lion Salt Works Trust, 2000.

Fielding, A. M., and Fielding, A. P. *Salt Works and Salinas. The Archaeology, Conservation and Recovery of Salt Making Sites and Their Processes.* Research Report No. 2, Lion Salt Works Trust, 2005.

Hardy, W. M. *Old Swanage and Purbeck Past and Present.* Dorchester County Chronicle, 1910.

Hughes, E. *Studies in Administration and Finance 1558–1825.* Manchester University Press, 1954; reprinted Porcupine Press, 1980.

Hurst, J. D. *Excavations at Upwich.* CBA Research Report 107, Council for British Archaeology, 1997.

Kurlansky, M. *Salt: A World History.* Jonathan Cape, 2002.

Lane, T., and Morris, E. L. *A Millennium of Salt Making: Prehistoric and Romano-British Salt Making Production in the Fenland.* Lincolnshire Archaeology and Heritage Reports Series No. 4. Heritage Trust of Lincolnshire, 2001.

Lloyd, Arthur. *The Salterns of the Lymington Area.* Buckland Trust, reprinted 1996.

Nevell, M., and Fielding, A. P. 'Brine in Britannia'. *Archaeology North West*, volume 7, issue 17. Council for British Archaeology North West, Lion Salt Works Trust and University of Manchester Archaeology Unit, 2005.

Whatley, C. A. *The Scottish Salt Industry 1570–1850. An Economic and Social History.* Aberdeen University Press, 1987.

Wilkinson, P. F.; Lockock, M.; and Sell, S. 'A Sixteenth Century Saltworks at Port Eynon, Gower'. *Post Medieval Archaeology*, 32, pages 3–32, 1998.

Williamson, R. *The Saga of the Southwold Salt Makers.* Privately published, 1999.

Woodiwiss, S. (editor). *Iron Age and Roman Salt Production and the Medieval Town of Droitwich.* CBA Research Report 81. Council for British Archaeology, 1992.

Yeoman, P. (editor). *The Salt and Coal Industries at St Monans, Fife, in the Eighteenth and Nineteenth Centuries.* Tayside and Fife Archaeological Committee, Monograph 2, Glenrothes, 1999.

Historic documents

Agricola, G. *De Re Metallica* (1555). Translated by H. C. Hoover and L. H. Hoover. Dover, 1950.

Brereton, Sir William. *Travels in Holland, the United Provinces, England, Scotland and Ireland.* Edited by Edward Hawkins. The Chetham Society, Volume I, 1844.

Salt Making in Cheshire (CD-ROM). Cheshire Family History Society, 2005. Contains reprint of Brownrigg, *The Art of Making Salt* (1748), and Calvert, *Salt in Cheshire* (E. & F. Spon, 1915).

This photograph of the inland solar salt works at Salinas de Añana, Álava, Spain, shows the system of brine channels which has operated there from the eighth century to the present day. The authority of Álava is managing a conservation programme to preserve the salt valley at Añana by continuing to manufacture salt.

Places to visit

Visitors are advised to check the opening times of museums before travelling and also to confirm that relevant items will be on display.

Calf of Eday, Orkney. This field monument comprises remains of a sixteenth-century salt works on the uninhabited Calf of Eday, off Eday.

Carrickfergus Museum and Civic Centre, 11 Antrim Street, Carrickfergus, Northern Ireland BT38 7DG. Telephone: 028 9335 8049. Website: www.carrickfergus.org
This is a museum of local history.

Catalyst, Mersey Road, Widnes, Cheshire WA8 0DF. Telephone: 0151 420 1121. Website: www.catalyst.org.uk
The corner of an iron salt pan from the Palmer-Mann salt works, Sandbach, can be found outside the museum. The exhibitions link salt with the modern chemical industry.

Colchester Castle Museum, Castle Park, Colchester, Essex CO1 1TJ. Telephone: 01206 282939. Website: www.colchestermuseums.org.uk
Material relating to prehistoric salt making is held in the reserve collection, viewable by appointment.

The Collection, Art and Archaeology in Lincolnshire, Danes Terrace, Lincoln LN2 1LP. Telephone: 01522 550990. Website: www.lincolnshire.gov.uk
The display of sea salt making in Lincolnshire covers all periods but concentrates on the prehistoric and Roman. Extensive collections on salt making are viewable by appointment.

Crosscanonby, Cumbria. Websites: www.allerdale.gov.uk and www.solwaycoastaonb.org.uk
There are remains of a sixteenth-century salt works with foundations of the salter's house and kinches for holding sleech. This field monument is on the coast road north of Maryport, adjoining the car park for the Roman milecastle.

Droitwich Brine Spa Complex, St Andrew's Road, Droitwich, Worcestershire WR9 8DN. Telephone: 01905 793446. Website: www.brinebath.co.uk
This modern health spa complex taps the town's underground brine spring for use in an indoor heated brine pool.

Droitwich Heritage Centre, St Richard's House, Victoria Square, Droitwich, Worcestershire WR9 8DS. Telephone: 01905 774312. Website: www.worcestershire.gov.uk
There are displays about the Droitwich salt industry from pre-Roman times. There is a reconstruction of the medieval brine pump at Vines Park.

Fleetwood Museum, Queen's Terrace, Fleetwood, Lancashire FY7 6BT. Telephone: 01253 876621. Website: www.lancashire.gov.uk
The ICI Gallery has a walk-through reconstruction of a rock salt mine.

Kimmeridge Bay, Dorset. Website: www.jurassiccoastline.com
There is an interpretation board on the coastal footpath. Car parking on the Smedmore Estate.

Lion Salt Works, Ollershaw Lane, Marston, Northwich, Cheshire CW9 6ES. Telephone: 01606 41823. Website: www.lionsaltworkstrust.co.uk
A trust is working to preserve this open pan salt works on the Trent & Mersey Canal, built in 1894 and closed in 1986. The pan houses, brine pump, brine tank, manager's office, smithy and railway siding survive. The trust has saved the hydraulic jacks used by the Brine Board to lift framed buildings in Northwich. Exhibition rooms include three lead salt pans from Bostock. The trust holds demonstrations of historic salt making.

Middlewich Library, Lewin Street, Middlewich, Cheshire CW10 9AS. Telephone: 01606 832801. Website: www.cheshire.gov.uk/library
There is a small display of finds from Roman salt-making sites in Middlewich.

Nantwich Museum, Pillory Street, Nantwich, Cheshire CW5 5BQ. Telephone: 01270 627104. Website: www.nantwichmuseum.org.uk
A history of Nantwich covers salt making since Roman times and includes a lead salt pan.

Nantwich Outdoor Brine Pool, Wall Lane, Nantwich, Cheshire CW5 5LS. Telephone: 01270 610606. Website: www.crewe-nantwich.gov.uk
The heated pool, opened in 1934, is probably the only inland outdoor brine pool left in the United Kingdom. Brine is pumped from the natural brine spring used by medieval salt-makers.

Port Eynon, Gower, South Wales. Website: www.the-gower.com
The field monument comprises a salt house and is protected from coastal erosion. It was surveyed by the Royal Commission on the Ancient and Historic Monuments of Wales, which holds the archive for the built heritage of Wales. (RCAHMW, Crown Building, Plas Crug, Aberystwyth, Ceredigion SY23 1NJ. Telephone: 01970 621200. Website: www.rcahmw.gov.uk)

St Barbe Museum, New Street, Lymington, Hampshire SO41 9BH. Telephone: 01590 676969. Website: www.stbarbe-museum.org.uk
Displays cover local sea salt making traditions. Salterns are still visible.

St Monans, Fife. Contact: Archaeological Unit, Development Services, Fife House, North Street, Glenrothes, Fife KY7 5LT. Telephone: 01592 413563.
There is a windmill with nine ruined pan house buildings and rock-cut brine tanks on the foreshore, accessible from the coastal footpath. The East Neuk of Fife Preservation Society opens the tower mill in the afternoons during July and August. At other times a key is available locally.

Salford City Art Gallery, Peel Park, The Crescent, Salford M5 4WU. Telephone: 0161 778 0800. Website: www.salford.gov.uk/salfordmuseum
An oil painting of Cheshire salt workers by Philip Homan Miller is on display. It was presented by Lady Ellis Lever in 1884.

The Salt Museum, 162 London Road, Northwich, Cheshire CW9 8AB. Telephone: 01606 41331. Website: www.saltmuseum.org.uk
Salt industry displays include a lead salt pan and a large scale model of a Middlewich open pan salt works. The corner of an iron salt pan from the Palmer-Mann salt works, Sandbach, is located outside the museum. The River Weaver Gallery includes the local history of mid Cheshire.

Southwold Museum, 9-11 Victoria Street, Southwold, Suffolk IP18 6HZ. Telephone: 01502 726097. Website: www.southwoldmuseum.org
A history of Southwold includes the development of salt making.

Staffordshire County Museum. Website: www.staffspasttrack.org.uk
A collection salvaged from the salt works in Staffordshire is held in the archives of the Staffordshire County Museum. Photographs and archives are available online.

Upton Country Park, Poole, Dorset BH17 7BJ. Telephone: 01202 262748. Website: www.poole.gov.uk
The park has a reconstructed Roman farm building based on excavations carried out at Poole Harbour on a potter's or salt worker's cottage, but this is open only to pre-booked school parties. It has been used for experimental Roman salt working and for Roman kiln firings.

Waterfront Museum, Culture and Community Learning Services, 4 High Street, Poole, Dorset BH15 1BW. Telephone: 01202 262600. Website: www.boroughofpoole.com
Re-opening in 2007 after refurbishment, the museum's changing displays may sometimes include Roman salt making.

Index